SOCIAL SCIENCE SEMINAR SERIES

Raymond H. Muessig and Vincent R. Rogers, Editors

THE VOLUMES AND THE AUTHORS

The Study of Anthropology, Pertti J. Pelto

Political Science: An Informal Overview, Francis J. Sorauf

Geography: Its Scope and Spirit, Jan O. M. Broek

Sociology: The Study of Man in Society, Caroline B. Rose

The Nature and the Study of History, Henry Steele Commager

Economics and Its Significance, Richard S. Martin and
  Reuben G. Miller

THE CONSULTANTS FOR THE SERIES

Anthropology, George D. Spindler

Political Science, Charles S. Hyneman

Geography, Jan O. M. Broek

Sociology, Arnold M. Rose

History, Henry Steele Commager

Economics, Kenneth E. Boulding

GEOGRAPHY

ITS SCOPE AND SPIRIT

Jan O. M. Broek

Department of Geography
University of Minnesota

With a Concluding Chapter Suggesting Methods
for Elementary and Secondary Teachers
by **Raymond H. Muessig** *and* **Vincent R. Rogers**

CHARLES E. MERRILL BOOKS, INC.   COLUMBUS, OHIO

Library of Congress Catalog Card Number: 65–21171

PRINTED IN THE UNITED STATES OF AMERICA

Social Science Seminar Series

Edited by Raymond H. Muessig
and Vincent R. Rogers

The Social Science Seminar Series presents scholarly viewpoints on and information about history, geography, political science, economics, sociology, and anthropology. This social science material is complemented by creative and practical methods, tailored to each of the individual fields, for elementary and secondary teachers.

One assumption built into these six volumes is that the social studies program in our schools should reflect more faithfully and sensitively the social sciences from which it is derived. It is imperative, then, that social scientists contribute their suggestions regarding over-all content selection problems in the social studies.

A second premise inherent in the Social Science Seminar Series is that professional educators are responsible for translating appropriate social science substance into meaningful and enriching learning experiences for children and youth. In their contacts with the editors of this Series, the contributing social scientists repeatedly made the point that they could discuss their disciplines only as they saw them and not in the light of what should be done with them in the schools. It is the professional educator—thoroughly prepared and broadly experienced in thinking about and coping with educational theories, problems, and practices—who must weld a framework that will support understandings, skills, attitudes, and appreciations drawn from or tied to the social science disciplines. It is the educator, too, who must decide what can and should be taught at various grade levels and how this subject matter might be conveyed, buttressed, and assessed by a myriad of suitable methods, materials, resources, and evaluative processes.

There is a critical need in both pre-service and in-service teacher education programs for up-to-date, clear, stimulating material concerned with recent developments in the social sciences. Teachers should see these disciplines as spheres of continuing scientific study and inquiry, rather than as hardened, static, sterile bodies of accumulated fact. Further, they must obtain a more sophisticated grasp of the goals, scope, importance, and interpretation of these fields as well as some understanding of the concerns faced by those working in a given field. The Social Science Seminar Series encourages and assists teachers at all instructional levels to critically examine their purposes in and approaches to the teaching of specific areas of content fundamentally related to the disciplines treated.

With this perspective in mind, the editors of the Series suggested that each of the contributing social scientists ask himself what his field really does contain that professional educators should consider teaching to youngsters. Each author was asked to describe the nature of his field; to trace briefly its history, development, and maturation; and to look at its unique methods of working as well as those procedures shared with other social sciences and related fields. Most importantly, each specialist was requested to select out of mountains of data a series of fundamental, compelling ideas that have emerged from his field.

In each volume of the Social Science Seminar Series, the editors have written a final chapter to accompany the discussions and analyses of the social scientists. The editors have *not* attempted to build an overarching theory of social studies education; rather, they have concentrated upon specific, functional classroom methods. The concluding chapters in this Series, therefore, do not present a total program, a master theory, a blanket plan of attack, or an endorsement of the proposals of any single group endeavoring to improve social studies instruction. The generalizations the editors have chosen to illustrate should not be viewed as the basis for a course or sequence of offerings. The ideas they have introduced transcend particular topics, units, themes, or curricula. Careful exposure to them can support many learnings. The editors have not dealt at this time with *why, how much, where,* and *when* questions regarding the place of individual social sciences in the social studies family today or tomorrow. As they see it, each social science can be taught by itself in breadth or depth, woven into existing scope and sequence patterns for development or supplementary purposes, or assigned manifold roles in some yet-to-be-developed curriculum design.

Space limitations have not permitted the exhaustive treatment of a single idea, problem, or approach drawn from each of the social sciences represented. Instead, the editors have suggested a number of procedures that could be used or adapted for use in a variety of elementary and secondary school situations. It is not intended that the techniques offered in the Series be employed in a one-a-day, isolated, disjointed, decontextualized fashion. A superficial flitting from one major insight to another would have little meaning for students and would possess limited retention or transfer value. It is not expected that pupils will comprehend abstract generalizations in a definitive sense after an occasional lesson or two. The editors believe that global ideas should be approached, discovered, introduced, developed, and confirmed in different ways and contexts and at increased levels of complexity throughout the school years. They have taken into account the fact that it takes time, patience, and systematic organization to build durable learning.

The Social Science Seminar Series, then, should function as a point of embarkation—inspiring and challenging readers to keep abreast of developments in the social sciences and in social studies education.

Editors'
Preface

While geography as an academic field cannot be claimed as the exclusive possession of the social sciences, certainly no series devoted to the social sciences and their transmission through social studies programs in elementary and secondary schools would be complete without the inclusion of this discipline. When the editors conceived the idea of the Social Science Seminar Series, they reserved a definite, prominent place for geography. They have been extremely fortunate in persuading an internationally known geographer to assume the major responsibility for this volume.

Like the other volumes in the Social Science Seminar Series, this book blends the reflections, viewpoints, and conclusions of a social scientist and two social studies educators. Dr. Jan O. M. Broek, Professor of Geography at the University of Minnesota, wrote the first six chapters, which deal with geography per se. Dr. Raymond H. Muessig, Professor of Education at The Ohio State University, and Dr. Vincent R. Rogers, Associate Professor of Education at the University of Minnesota, composed the final chapter, which suggests methods for classroom teachers.

Professor Broek has put forth many seminal ideas that readers will want to consider further. He has also suggested a number of sources worthy of continued independent study. The editors feel that this book will be both intellectually and professionally rewarding.

Raymond H. Muessig
Vincent R. Rogers

Author's
Preface

Professional geographers, like their colleagues in other fields, become so engrossed in research and teaching that all too often they neglect to explain in non-technical language the aims, methods, deeds, and rewards of their discipline. I hope that this volume will help to bridge this gap in communication. For this purpose I have tried to present the various currents of thought in contemporary American geography and to draw attention to a variety of substantive studies. Even so, the book expresses ·a personal view, gained over many years of participation in professional geography here and abroad.

I gratefully acknowledge my debt to co-workers in the field, past and present. If I had traced all ideas to their origin, this book would have been peppered with footnotes. Instead, mindful of the prospective audience, I have in the main restricted references to those that may serve as guides to further reading. I appreciate the courtesy of those who have allowed me to use direct quotations and reproductions of maps; specific acknowledgments are given in the appropriate places. My thanks go to Mr. and Mrs. Fred E. Lukermann, who assisted in the initial stage of the project. The enthusiasm, encouragement, and skillful assistance of the editors of this Series, Dr. Raymond H. Muessig and Dr. Vincent R. Rogers, added to the pleasure I found in writing this book. In preparing the manuscript, my wife has gone far beyond the call of duty, undaunted by the anguished cries of the author who seemed to believe that he had expressed his thoughts in perfect form.

Jan O. M. Broek

Table
of
Contents

Geographic Thought and Practice

chapter one

VALUE OF GEOGRAPHY

Early in the Second World War President Roosevelt, in one of his "fireside chats" by radio, asked his audience to look at a world map while he explained the threats to the United States of hostile encirclement if the Axis powers were to win. More recently President Kennedy appeared on the television screen and pointed out on a wall map the strategic importance of Laos and Vietnam in Southeast Asia and the significance of this area in world affairs. Both Presidents were, in fact, discussing geographic concepts of location and of interrelations between parts of the earth.

But geographic knowledge is equally important, though less dramatic in meaning, in peacetime. Projects for the advance of underdeveloped countries, or of depressed areas at home, require understanding of the local way of life and of the interconnections of human and material resources. Or, if we want our cities to be more efficient and more beautiful we must begin with analyzing their present plan and structure. Thus we start with learning their geography. That is, we make a map showing the location of the central business district, the industrial areas, the various residential sections, the parks, and the transportation system—or chaos—that connects all parts of the city and links it with other places.

In all these cases we want to know what a country, a region, or a place is like and what its relations are with other places. And thinking of places (as a shorthand term for all areas, large or small), we always see in our minds a group of people on a piece of land, not like actors on a stage, but as folk whose lives are closely tied to their homeland and strongly conditioned by their location among other lands and peoples.

1

Geography is not merely useful. It is exciting for its own sake. Making one's first trip through another part of the United States, or traveling abroad, who has not been aroused to ask such questions as: What caused these waterfalls along the valley's rim? Why are the fields like a checkerboard here while yesterday we rarely saw a rectangular field? What keeps people in this "God-forsaken" place? Or, what is the reason for all the building activity in this area? Why do farmers live together in a village instead of out on their land? Why is the layout and style of farmsteads here so different from those we saw this morning? Is it just an impression or the truth that we notice a change in racial type?

In a less strenuous way we gather geographic knowledge vicariously through reading about the adventures of others. Our forefathers were fascinated by the tales of heroic voyages and discoveries as published by Hakluyt. A generation ago Richard Halliburton was popular. And who does not know about Thor Heyerdahl and his Kon-Tiki expedition? The large and loyal audience of the *National Geographic Magazine* reflects the wide interest in distant places, if only because of its excellent photographs. Such books as Rachel Carson's masterfully written *The Sea Around Us* and Alan Moorehead's deft descriptions of *The Blue Nile* and *The White Nile* are also essentially geographic. Nor should we forget the regional novel which, if worthy of the name, depicts life in a specific environment. Thomas Hardy's stories have their setting in southwestern England, and Joseph Conrad gives us a feeling for the South Pacific. American literature abounds in tales of the struggle to build a home in a new country, such as *A Son of the Middle Border* and *Giants in the Earth.*

There are, of course, many gradations between pure curiosity at the one extreme and the direct usefulness of geography at the other. Somewhere in between lies the value of geography as part of the intellectual equipment of every citizen of every country. In particular, how can the citizens of the United States, a great world power and a democracy, exercise their rights and perform their duties if they are geographically illiterate? All too frequently, when a conflict breaks out somewhere in the world we are completely taken by surprise because we were not aware of long smoldering friction between minorities, old territorial claims, fast population growth on top of miserable living conditions, coveted mineral wealth, or strategic pass routes. How many Americans understood the significance of Korea's location in 1950? How many have looked on a map to find Quemoy and its relation to Formosa and mainland China? Why was Katanga not just another bit of rain forest in the Congo civil war? And why does Sweden not join the other Scandinavian countries in the North Atlantic Treaty Organization?

The answers require some geographic knowledge. Instead some people prefer to divide the world into two ideological camps, "Free" and "Communist," as the sole and simple basis for their opinion on what America should or should not do.

At home, too, we need better geographic understanding to solve our domestic problems. Depopulation of agricultural areas, rapid growth of the suburbs, change in character of the central business districts, Negro migration, exhaustion of mineral resources, pollution of air and streams, and other matters of concern must be understood better by the general public so that it will actively support efforts toward solution. Above all—and this is true of international as well as national affairs— problems must be seen in their regional context. Justice, freedom, democracy, and equal rights are high ideals. Their wise application demands an awareness of different conditions in different places. "Global unity" does not mean world-wide uniformity. We must not simply assume that our own interpretation of ideals is the right one which we can confidently project on all other peoples as the standard model for imitation. Awareness of conditions and ways of life in other countries helps us to frame more realistic attitudes.

GEOGRAPHY'S POSITION AMIDST THE SCIENCES

The division of all fields of learning into physical, biological, and social sciences and humanities is, of course, no more than a rough classification. It is not to be expected that each individual discipline will fit neatly into one pigeonhole. Geographers in general consider their field to be first and foremost a social science, but many value highly its bonds with the physical and biological sciences. Others emphasize its common spirit with the humanities.

Our present purpose is to see where geography stands among the social sciences. Here again we must remember that there are no sharp lines of demarcation. After all, the social sciences as we know them today all stem from a common pool of knowledge. Moreover, their development has varied in different countries. Cultural traditions, domestic problems, and intellectual leadership have affected the nature of each social science and altered the emphasis, and thus the division of tasks, between the fields. We can, therefore, define each social science only by its core, not by fixing exact boundaries. What then gives geography, in essence, a character of its own? What distinguishes it from the other social sciences? It is its concern with the character of "place," that is, the integrated whole of a people and its habitat, and the interrelations between places. Or putting the emphasis differently, one might say that geography is orderly knowledge of the diversity of the earth as the world of man.

Most sciences specialize in one particular set of phenomena: plants, rocks, economic or political behavior, and the like. The workers in these fields are puzzled by the efforts and claims of geography. They feel that the geographer seems to put his nose into any and every subject which is already taken care of by the specialized sciences. They ask: When the geographer studies the distribution of wheat or steel mills is he not trespassing in the field of economics? Similarly, are his observations on the suburban explosion not sociology? And those on nomadism not anthropology? From their point of view geography is merely a scissors-and-paste job of putting together the findings of other sciences.

It is curious that the study of history seldom suffers from this lack of understanding. The historian makes no claim to any specific category of facts; on the contrary, he uses any data that may help to understand an historical event, from psychology to economics and from weather to soils. The similarity with geography is clear. Both are essentially interested in comprehending wholes, but the historian thinks mainly in time bonds, the geographer in place bonds. Critics are, therefore, bagging their own decoys when they shoot at the multitude of facts the geographer uses. He does not study peoples, crops, customs, minerals, towns, or house types for their own sake, but because he perceives them as parts of an interrelated complex that give character to a place. It is the place (region or country, if you wish) that he wants to understand. No other social science does this.

But there remain further doubts concerning the worth of geography, and these are expressed not only outside the profession. First of all, in an age of ever more specialized research is there a place for a discipline that insists on taking a comprehensive view of earth and man? Our obviously biased answer is: There is indeed. Perhaps geography is bucking the spirit of the time, but its way of looking at the world counterbalances artificial partitions. The greater the fragmentation of knowledge, the more need there is for putting the bits together again in an orderly way to understand the reality of places.

These reflections raise another question. One may accept the value of geography as an intellectual viewpoint that should be part of everyone's education. But is it worthy of the name of *Science*? Avoiding the quicksand of semantics, we will take the question to mean simply whether geography does what science is supposed to do, such as to find cause and effect, seek generalizations, develop theoretical concepts, and perhaps even to predict. Few sciences actually come up to what the layman expects from them in these matters, but that does not invalidate the question. In truth, we must admit that geography appears weak .in theory if one compares it with a field like economics, not to speak of physics. But is it fair to compare geography with fields that have an entirely different orientation?

Geography does generalize, but in ways relevant to its own problems. One procedure is to group like phenomena in categories (climates, crops, settlements, occupations) and to find relationships between the various categories over the whole earth or its parts. For instance, the relationship between climate and vegetation is fairly well established. Or, with more caution, it can be stated that there is a connection between type of economy and birth rate, between income per capita and diet. Geography shares the discovery of such relationships with other sciences. The geographer, however, puts them to work in dividing the earth into meaningful parts. For instance, the similar patterns of a series of four world maps depicting for each country per capita income, calorie intake, power use, and the proportion of the labor force employed in agriculture present an instructive starting point for generalizations on the so-called developed and underdeveloped countries.

THE MEANING OF "PLACE"

The "places" geography studies are of two kinds. First of all, place means a specific, unique area, identified as such by its given name, be it Illinois or Istanbul, Mount Whitney or Hudson Bay. Each such "place-individual" is listed in the index of an atlas, usually with its "address" expressed in degrees of longitude and latitude.

Examples of the second kind of "place" are plateau, desert, mixed farming, and metropolitan areas. Each of these terms designates a species of a class or genus, organized on some principle of likeness or relationship. Such places are not "given." They are mental concepts formulated to arrange earth features in some abstract order. The word "region" is usually restricted to this type of place. It is an area of any size that is homogeneous in terms of the specific criteria of its class.

A century ago the teaching of geography concentrated largely on identifying the place-individuals ("New York is bounded by . . . The capital of the State is Albany. On what river lies Albany?" . . . and so forth). Knowledge of specific places is as essential now as then—one wishes schools would pay more attention to it—but it has been joined by the more penetrating regional analysis. The two complement each other. A country is better understood if we analyze it by generic regions; in turn, generic regions are related to the earth by reference to specific places. For instance, Illinois belongs, in terms of climate (the generic order), to the humid continental type (or species); in regard to agriculture it is part of the mixed farming region or "corn belt"; its manufacturing industries make it part of the main American manufacturing zone.

Whatever the kind of place, we must always keep in mind its position in time as well as its location in space. A place cannot be understood by merely observing the interaction of present-day forces. Knowing the legacy of the past and sensing the presence of change are essential qualities of the geographic mind. As to location, no place exists in isolation. We must, therefore, look beyond the internal nature of the area itself (the site) to perceive its external relations with other areas (the situation). For example, the Arctic has few advantages of site but has gained vital strategic importance because of its situation between adversaries, both armed with intercontinental missiles.

CAREERS IN GEOGRAPHY

Some eighty universities in the United States offer graduate study in geography, of which about thirty have programs leading to the doctor's degree. Professionally trained geographers qualify for a great variety of jobs. The majority engage in teaching and research at institutions of higher learning. There are, however, hundreds of geographers with M.A. and Ph.D. degrees in government, business, and industry. Those in government service scrutinize agricultural, industrial, and recreational land use, regional population trends, mineral and water resources; they supervise map libraries and, of course, make maps of any and all things mappable.

Geographers in increasing numbers work in government planning agencies, from city to national level, or in private planning consultant firms. Analysis of spatial patterns of population, economic activities, land utilization, and of the underlying social-economic forces is the prerequisite for planning a better environment. Geography, with its concern for place and place relationships, finds here rewarding service in the interest of public welfare. Private business employs geographers as experts to select sites for enterprises from industrial plants to supermarkets. Transportation and tourist agencies use some geographers and could use more. Quite a few geographers hold positions in publishing firms, mainly in those that produce maps and atlases.

During the Second World War a multitude of geographers helped the war effort by preparing written reports and maps on climatic conditions in various parts of the world, enemy industrial targets, landing beaches, potential battle terrains, and on other strategic matters. Much of this intelligence work continues into the present, joined by studies on geographic aspects of foreign aid, such as resource development.

These examples suffice to support the contention that professional work in geography is not a tightly drawn circle where teachers train teachers. For the geographer the world lies open. He ventures forth wherever his interests lead, an expert with curiosity and a skill that is of relevance and value to the world.

Suggested Readings

Hartshorne, Richard. *The Nature of Geography: A Critical Survey of Current Thought in the Light of the Past.* First published in *Annals of the Association of American Geographers,* 29 (1939), 173–658; issued as a book (Lancaster, Pa., 1939) and reprinted by the Association of American Geographers (A.A.G.) at various dates. Available in the Central Office of the Association, 1146 16th St. N.W., Washington 36, D.C.
   This is a monumental work, but difficult for the uninitiated.

*————. *Perspective on the Nature of Geography.* Chicago: Rand McNally & Co. for the A.A.G., 1959. 201 pp.
   A more concise and positive statement than the above book, with some amendments on earlier views.

*James, P. E., and C. F. Jones (eds.). *American Geography: Inventory and Prospect.* Syracuse, N.Y.: Syracuse University Press for the A.A.G., 1954. 590 pp.
   A cooperative effort by many geographers to explain the discipline and its subdivisions to a wide audience. Excellent bibliographies accompany each chapter.

Freeman, T. W. *A Hundred Years of Geography.* Chicago: Aldine Publishing Co., 1962. 335 pp.
   A factual survey by a British geographer.

Taylor, Griffith (ed.). *Geography in the Twentieth Century.* New York: Philosophical Library, Inc., 1951; 3d enlarged ed., 1957.
   Good essays on various aspects of geography, although one may differ with the editor's environmentalist views.

Wooldridge, S. W., and W. G. East. *The Spirit and Purpose of Geography.* London & New York: Hutchinson's University Library, 1951. 176 pp.
   A brief well-written presentation by two British geographers, with more emphasis on physical geography than in the American publications.

---

* Throughout this book asterisks indicate titles highly recommended to laymen and social studies teachers who want to gather a small library on geography.

AMERICAN GEOGRAPHIC PERIODICALS

The Geographical Review. Quarterly, $9.50 per year. The American Geographical Society of New York, Broadway & 156th St., New York 32, N.Y.

Focus. Monthly, except July and August; $1.25 a year, $3 for 3 years. The A.G.S. (above).

Very valuable for teachers; it presents background facts, maps, and interpretations of current problem areas by specialists in the subject.

Annals of the Association of American Geographers. Quarterly, $10 a year. The A.A.G.

Equal in quality to *The Geographical Review,* but more likely to confront the reader with papers on methodological and philosophical subjects.

The Professional Geographer (Forum and Journal of the A.A.G.). 6 nos. a year, $5.

Contains short articles, official notices and reports, news of members and centers of geographic work.

Economic Geography. Quarterly, $8 a year. Clark University, Worcester, Mass.

Géographe Canadien. Quarterly, $7 a year. The Canadian Association of Geographers. Order from: Secretary, C.A.G., Morrice Hall, McGill University, Montreal 2, P.Q. Canada.

The scholarly journal of Canadian geographers.

The Journal of Geography. Monthly, except June, July, August; $5 a year. The National Council for Geographic Education (N.C.G.E.). Order from: A. J. Nystrom & Co., 3333 Elston Ave., Chicago 18, Ill. Devoted to geography in education; contains articles of substantive as well as didactic nature.

Landscape. 3 times a year, $3 a year. J. B. Jackson, Box 2323, Santa Fe, N.M.

An attractive and stimulating journal concerning man's impact on the land.

National Geographic Magazine. Monthly, $8 a year. The National Geographic Society, 17th & M Sts. N.W., Washington, D.C.

A popular journal with fine photographs and general reference maps.

OTHER MATERIALS

Current Geographical Publications. Additions to the Research Catalogue of the A.G.S. (mimeographed). Monthly, except July and August; $8 a year. For address see under *Geographical Review,* above.

The most comprehensive guide to the geographic literature published in English.

A Career in Geography. The Joint Committee on Careers of the A.A.G. and N.C.G.E., 1962. Printed and distributed as a service to education . . . (by) Denoyer-Geppert Co., 5235 Ravenswood Ave., Chicago 40, Ill.

A popularly written useful pamphlet.

Augelli, John (ed.). *American Geography, 1960–63: Education, Employment and Other Trends.* A.A.G., 1964. Available from Central Office, Association of American Geographers, 1146 16th St. N.W., Washington 36, D.C.

*Espenshade, E. B. (ed.). *Goode's World Atlas.* Chicago: Rand McNally & Co., 1964.

This widely used atlas, now in its twelfth edition, is a much better geographic tool than many high priced reference atlases sold in regular book stores to the general public.

*Williams, J. E. (ed.). *The Prentice-Hall World Atlas.* 2d ed. Englewood Cliffs, N.J.: Prentice-Hall, Inc., 1962.

Much the same can be said about this atlas as the previous one. A third edition will soon appear. The shaded relief maps, derived from a European cartographic institute, are particularly attractive, but there are fewer topical maps than in *Goode's World Atlas.*

Bartholomew, J. (ed.). *The Edinburgh World Atlas; or Advanced Atlas of Modern Geography.* 4th ed. Edinburgh: J. Bartholomew and Son, 1962.

Lewis, C. and J. D. Campbell (eds.). *The American Oxford Atlas.* New York: Oxford University Press, 1951.

The latter two atlases are fine British products, moderately priced, in line with the two American atlases mentioned above.

Coan, O. W., and R. G. Lillard. *America in Fiction: An annotated list of novels that interpret aspects of life in the United States.* 4th ed. Stanford, Calif.: Stanford University Press, 1956.

This is a valuable source for regional novels to supplement geographic description.

Development
of Geographic chapter two
Thought

The ancient Greeks built their conception of the universe on what they had learned from earlier civilizations in the Middle East, but their own contributions were so novel and far reaching that we may start with them for this brief historical survey.[1]

GEOGRAPHY IN ANTIQUITY

Any scientific endeavor depends first and foremost on careful observation. Here the Greeks led the way. They described the lay of the land as well as the character and customs of the inhabitants. Herodotus (484–425 B.C.) was not only "the father of history" but also of geography because he always placed historic events in their geographic setting. Not only did the Greeks give descriptions of places (the so-called *topographies*) but they also attempted to explain them. Herodotus, for example, having observed the black soil along the Nile, linked it to the silt dropped by the river on its flood plain. Also, having noted that the Nile flood plain extends into the sea in the form of a triangle, like the Greek letter *delta*, he reasoned that it must be due to the deposition of river mud.

Events occur and places exist at specific locations on the earth's surface. The Greeks had concluded that the earth was a sphere, and later Eratosthenes (276–194 B.C.) calculated its circumference with remarkable accuracy. His genuinely geographic contribution, however,

---

[1] Most books in the reading list at the end of Chapter 1 contain material pertaining to the development of geographic thought, and bibliographic references. An excellent introduction is P. E. James' article "Geography" in the Encyclopaedia Britannica.

10

was to devise a system of lines of latitude and longitude on which he plotted the location of seas, lands, mountains, rivers, and towns. Thus the real map—in contrast to a mere sketch—was born: geographic order replaced unco-ordinated description.

Since the Greeks knew that the length of day and the height of the sun above the horizon differed with varying latitudes, they conceived a division of the earth in heat belts corresponding to zones of latitude (*klimata*). In this way arose the concept of the Torrid, Temperate, and Frigid Zones as belts defined by parallels, a climatic half-truth which echoes in the layman's mind to this very day. Although it is easy to point out these and other errors, the positive side of the Greek achievement is what counts. They observed and described places, plotted locations, organized data in meaningful categories, and developed theories to explain the world around them.

We owe our knowledge of Greek geographic thought largely to two masterful compilers of the Roman era, who in their diverging interests neatly present the two main aspects of classical geography. One was Strabo (64 B.C.–A.D. 20), whose *Geographia* was essentially an encyclopedic description of the known inhabited world—of the *ecumene*, to use the Greek term. The other was Ptolemy, who lived around A.D. 150. His primary interest was in the mathematical aspects of map construction and place location. He improved methods of map projection and introduced the terms "parallel" and "meridian" for the lines of latitude and longitude. Unfortunately he accepted the calculation of the earth's circumference by Posidonius (circa 100 B.C.) instead of the much more accurate one of Eratosthenes, thus representing the length of the equator —or any other great circle—as some 7,000 miles less than its actual size. Ptolemy made a gazetteer of all place names known to him and assigned to each its location by latitude and longitude. Even though the fixing of latitude (by means of the sun's position above the horizon at noon) was well known, it had been done for relatively few places; determination of longitude remained for many centuries little better than guesswork. It is no wonder, therefore, that Ptolemy erred in many of his place locations. Nevertheless, his image of the world—*Imago Mundi*—was the most complete drawn up to that time and continued to be so for centuries.

MIDDLE AGES AND RENAISSANCE

The term "Dark Ages" expresses well the regression of scientific learning in medieval Europe. Dogmatic justification of the Christian faith replaced free intellectual inquiry. The image of the world was molded to fit the Bible. Greek thought, if contrary to doctrine, had to be suppressed as pagan. The earth became a disk, with Jerusalem at its center.

In contrast, during the eighth and following centuries new zest for learning spread through the world of Islam. In the Moslem universities from Persia to Spain, scholars studied the Greek heritage. Arab traders traveled widely and .brought back new information which the scholars compared with Greek ideas or incorporated into Ptolemy's map. The most remarkable traveler was Ibn Batuta (1304–1368), whose voyages extended east as far as northern China and south along the east coast of Africa well beyond the equator. The latter venture brought empirical proof that Aristotle had been wrong in asserting that the Torrid Zone was too hot for human habitation. Even before that time the geographer Al Idrisi, or Edrisi (1099–1166), had realized that the Greek concept of five climatic zones did not fit reality and had proposed a much more refined system.

Ibn Khaldun (1332–1406), the last great Moslem scholar, wrote a remarkable historical geography, actually an embryonic science of society, which surpassed anything of its nature that had been written before or was to come in centuries thereafter. Especially interesting are his comparisons between the settled life in irrigated districts and the nomadic life of pastoral peoples in the surrounding dry lands. The pastoral nomads, well organized for mobile warfare, could build large empires by conquering the oasis dwellers. After a time the nomads would become absorbed in the way of life of the settled people, and their empires would fall apart. Thus Ibn Khaldun explained the rise and foresaw the fall of the Moslem empire. Modern geographers are particularly impressed with his cultural interpretation of the physical environment and his analysis of the role of the city in the regional economy. Unfortunately neither his writings nor those of Edrisi were translated into Latin or another Western language until the nineteenth century, and thus Europe, when it awoke from its medieval slumber, failed to notice them.

Europe also had had its travelers, but their impact on science had been virtually nil. Norsemen reached North America about 1000, but the news scarcely penetrated beyond the coastal communities of Scandinavia. Several missionaries and merchants (Marco Polo!) visited China, India, and other parts of Asia. Their accounts, eagerly read as wonderful tales, were hardly considered grist for the scholar's mill.

The Renaissance brought, as in other fields, the revival of classic geographic thought. Ptolemy's *Geography*, translated in Latin in the fifteenth century, made a deep impact in learned circles. That century saw the upsurge of Portuguese and Spanish exploration which culminated in the voyages to India and America. In planning new exploits the experts relied on Ptolemy as the great authority (witness Columbus, whose confidence in the great master led him to believe that he had reached Asia). As the knowledge of new lands proved Ptolemy wrong, another image of the world began to emerge. New map projections— particularly that of Mercator in 1569—as well as new world maps and globes reflected the shift from local horizon to world-wide perspective. In addition there appeared (just as in Greek antiquity) the travel accounts, which served as raw material for the compilers of encyclopedic volumes on world geography. (Today's library catalogues still recognize geography only under the heading "Geography and Travel," although one looks in vain for analogous sections in other fields, such as "Chemistry and Cooking.")

The man to recognize the need for new organization of geographic knowledge was Bernhardus Varenius, whose *Geographia Generalis* was published in Amsterdam in 1650, the year of his death at age twenty-eight. Varenius pointed out a dualism in geography which to some extent is still with us. In part, geography deals with processes and phenomena which are purely physical in nature, such as those pertaining to the lithosphere, hydrosphere, and atmosphere, as well as those depending on the relation of sun and earth. All these processes and the resulting features can be studied through the methods used in physics and mathematics and can be proved with scientific exactitude. On the other hand, geography also considers social-cultural phenomena, which are by nature not open to that kind of verification. Generalizations regarding human groups have more limited validity and always are statements of probability rather than certainty.

Because of this inner dualism, Varenius proposed a division between *general* and *special* geography. The former should deal with physical matters for which universal, earth-wide, laws could be formulated. The latter, special geography, should examine the particular areas or regions of the earth which derive their character from the interaction of human and physical processes. Varenius' book covered only general geography, but his preface sketched the program for the other section, "regional geography," as we would call it. Varenius' geography contained a double dualism: general versus special geography paralleled physical versus human geography. To put it in terms more familiar to the modern reader, Varenius seemed to suggest that general (systematic, topical) geography considers physical matters which can be explained by "laws," while special (regional) geography, since it involves unpredictable man, must remain largely descriptive.

BEGINNINGS OF MODERN GEOGRAPHY

Varenius had presented the structure of geography as a scientific discipline. It remained for Immanuel Kant (1724–1804) to secure its foundations within the framework of the contemporary philosophy of science. Moreover, he tested his views by teaching a course in geography for over three decades at the University of Königsberg. According to Kant, all knowledge can be organized from three different viewpoints. One of these is to sort the facts into groups according to the kind of objects studied. The disciplines that study these categories-as-such are the "systematic sciences." For instance, botany studies plants, geology the earth's crust, and sociology social groups. This approach, however, fails to exhaust the study of reality, according to Kant. A second way of looking at facts is to see them in their relationship through time. "Historical sciences" employ this viewpoint. And, thirdly, there is the study of things as they are associated in space. This is the domain of the "geographical sciences."

It is readily seen that in this philosophic construction geography gained an honorable status among the sciences. From Kant onward, this view has been stated and restated as the fundamental justification for geography. In the United States Richard Hartshorne—following the German geographer Alfred Hettner—made it the cornerstone of his learned treatise on *The Nature of Geography* (1939). Most American geographers accept Hartshorne's exposition of Kant's system. However, the development of non-Euclidean geometry and of relativity theories since the late nineteenth century raises questions about the validity of this threefold division of the sciences.

Without getting too involved in the philosophy of science, one may ask, for instance, whether the systematic (topical) sciences actually study phenomena without reference to time and space. Many geographers also deny that one can separate time and space in such fields as cultural geography. Although it is often asserted that geography deals with the present, we must examine the processes that work through time to understand that "present." Moreover, geographers want to know what places were like at an earlier time, without necessarily using that knowledge to explain the present. In turn, historians study past events in particular places. These comments may suffice to show that in modern thought the Kantian scheme is open to doubt. These changing viewpoints and challenges are reflected in current methodological controversies which lie beyond the scope of the present chapter.

While Kant's importance for geography lies mainly in his providing a philosophic justification, Alexander von Humboldt (1769–1859) and Carl Ritter (1779–1859), also German scholars, molded the substance of geography into scientific form. Von Humboldt was inspired by the wish to understand the complex totality of the universe. In this respect he was the last of the great cosmographers. At the same time he was a great explorer, especially of tropical America. Many sciences are in his debt for new facts and new insights, but geography claims him as one of its founding fathers. It does so because he strove to understand the inter-relationships between earth features that give a landscape its character.[2] By presenting explanatory descriptions of areas and by comparing them with other lands, he set the tone for scientific geography. This procedure contrasted with the jumble of political-statistical facts and place names which comprised the bulk of the geographic literature of that time.

Von Humboldt's principal interest was in physical and biological features, as demonstrated in his enormous output of studies, ranging from the results of his American explorations to the majestic *Cosmos*. He drew profiles of continental cross-sections, related vegetation to altitude zones, and used if not invented the "isotherm" (see p. 68) as the means to compare temperatures. However, he did not neglect the world of man. For instance, noting the absence of pastoral nomads in the Americas he questioned the popular view that this way of life was a universal stage in social evolution. He also commented on similarities between Asian and native American cultures and tried to explain them. Moreover, he wrote some treatises, in essence regional geographies, on Cuba and Mexico.

Carl Ritter's work complemented that of von Humboldt by empha-sizing human experience in the regional context. Although he traveled in Europe, he was more the armchair geographer who used the observa-tions of others to build his own structure. His great work, *Die Erdkunde*, was to be a regional description of the earth, of which, however, he completed only the many volumes on Asia and Europe. Ritter looked upon the earth as the home of man. He divided the earth into natural regions—mainly according to land forms—and examined their meaning for the society who occupied, or had occupied, each unit. "Meaning" is the right word here because Ritter was a deeply religious man. He thought that divine will had created the earth as a school for man, in which he would progress from crude barbarism to spiritual greatness.

---

2 *Views of Nature,* or *Aspects of Nature,* both translations of his *Ansichten der Natur* (1807). This book, which the author considered merely as a popular account of some of his impressions of South America, gives a good idea of his approach to geographic study.

Each part of the earth served a purpose in the march of progress.[3] The first civilizations arose in the river valleys of the Middle East. Then the center moved to Greece, later encompassing the entire Mediterranean Sea, and subsequently occupied the oceanic environment of northwestern Europe.

Carl Ritter has been criticized for mixing his religious philosophy of divine purpose with objective investigation. This, however, was quite common in his time. If one overlooks the teleological approach (that is, the concern with ultimate ends) there still remains a treasure of geographic insights. Ritter constantly strove to show each individual earth unit as a whole, as an interrelated areal complex of elements. So impressive was his method that his plan of study became the model for regional presentation. His influence can still be seen in some methods of teaching: define the area as a unit of the physical environment; put in man, and show how he, with the mental and material equipment at his command, adapts to and uses his habitat.

DIVERGENT VIEWS IN THE LATE NINETEENTH CENTURY

In the second half of the nineteenth century the expanding frontiers in the physical and biological sciences fascinated ever more students. In geography they concentrated on climate, plant and animal world, and above all on land forms (geomorphology). Most geographers of this period were trained as geologists and used geological methods in their research. By comparison, the geography of man languished. It stayed in the Ritterian tradition of describing man in relation to his habitat, but opened no new perspectives. The chair in geography which Ritter had held at the University of Berlin was not filled for many years. In England, too, the first chair in geography, briefly occupied by Alexander Maconochie in the 1830's, lapsed after his resignation. Some geographers wanted to make the discipline a preserve of pure science. Since human behavior did not appear to be subject to general laws, they proposed to exclude man entirely from the field of geography.

Outside of academic circles there were, nevertheless, stirrings which heralded new approaches to human geography. In the United States modern civilization assaulted nature by creating new landscapes and often abusing the resources. Major John Wesley Powell (1834–1902) explored the western lands and pioneered in the description and explana-

---

[3] Among the translations of parts of Ritter's work are two edited by W. L. Gage: *Geographical Studies* (1861) and *Comparative Geography* (1865). (New York: American Book Co.)

tion of land forms. However, his concern with practical matters of settlement led him far beyond the usual tasks of the geomorphologist. He clearly saw the risks which settlers faced as they moved into the dry lands. Unless irrigation was feasible, farms would have to be considerably larger than envisaged in the Homestead Act of 1862. Thus, Powell surveyed the land forms and water resources and proposed measures to insure their most efficient use.

Another American, better known through his writings than his deeds, but equaling Powell in influence, was George Perkins Marsh (1801–1882). Among his many interests was a deep concern for conservation of resources. In the introductory chapter of his main book [4] G. P. Marsh referred to the "new school of geographers" led by von Humboldt and Ritter, who sought to find out "how far external physical conditions . . . have influenced the social life and social progress of man." This, Marsh conceded, was indeed worthy of study, but he wanted to raise another question: How has man changed the earth? Marsh asserted that it was not the earth which made man, but man who made, or at least remade, the earth; and worse, man frequently destroyed his habitat by ruthless exploitation. His book, filled with case studies of the wanton use of resources from Roman times onward, warned Americans to exercise restraint in taming their vast domain, lest it be turned into wasteland like parts of the Old World. For this reason Marsh's book has been called "the fountainhead of the conservation movement in the United States."

Academic geography, engrossed in physical studies pure and simple, paid little attention to Marsh, even though he had demonstrated that man was an important agent in changing the face of the earth. Recognition by professional geographers came only in the 1930's, with the rise of cultural geography.[5]

The year 1859 marked not only the death of von Humboldt and Ritter but also the publication of Charles Darwin's *On the Origin of Species.* Darwin's ideas on adaptation to the environment and on evolution stimulated social scientists to reappraise old concepts. The Greeks had already linked national character to climate. Now observations in the biological sphere seemed to provide the key to scientific understanding of differences in cultural levels and economic activities. Among geographers it was, above all, Friedrich Ratzel (1844–1904) who explored

---

[4] *Man and Nature, or Physical Geography as Modified by Human Action* (New York: Scribners, 1864). The second edition (1874) had the more direct title *The Earth as Modified by Human Action.* The quotation is from the later edition, p. 7.

[5] In 1931 I found the second edition of Marsh's treatise in a bookstore in Berkeley. Intrigued by its title I bought it. No one among the geographers at the University of California to whom I showed it knew it.

the influences of physical environment on mankind.[6] The first volume of his *Anthropogeographie* appeared in 1882. Although the author admitted that other factors than those of nature shape the fate of a people, the burden of his presentation was that man is a creature of his environment, in much the same way as Darwin had demonstrated adaptation and survival of the fittest in the animal world.

Ratzel, however, was also a keen student of anthropology. Closer examination of different peoples must have convinced him that man is first and foremost conditioned by his cultural environment and that his reactions to nature differ sharply according to his culture. At any rate, his second volume of *Anthropogeographie* (1891) breathes a different spirit than the first. Now the emphasis is on distribution and density of population, forms of settlements, migrations of peoples, and diffusion of culture traits. For the explanation of these features Ratzel did not merely resort to environmental influences but equally, or more so, to historical-cultural factors. In one of his essays he underscores the paramount significance of the cultural factor by declaring: "I could perhaps understand New England without knowing the land, but never without knowing the Puritan immigrants." [7]

Ratzel's impact on American geographers was quite strong, owing to the rendition of his ideas by Ellen Churchill Semple, his American pupil, who taught at the University of Chicago and Clark University. Unfortunately Miss Semple stressed the environmental relationships and almost ignored Ratzel's second thoughts on this subject. Her books on *American History and its Geographic Conditions* (1903) and on *Influences of Geographic Environment* (1911) are classics of their kind, but distress the modern geographer in their overemphasis on the earth's effects on man.

Miss Semple was not alone in conceiving human geography as the study of environmental influences. In fact, she rose to eminence because she expressed forcefully and clearly the viewpoint of her American colleagues. The man most influential in shaping this common attitude was William Morris Davis, dean of American geographers in the early twentieth century. His scientific contribution lies in his spelling out the evolution of land forms through stages of young, mature, and old relief. Though his domain obviously was in physical geography, he was quite willing to give the study of man a place in the discipline. How, then,

---

[6] H. Wanklyn, *Friedrich Ratzel, a Biographical Memoir and Bibliography* (New York: Cambridge University Press, 1961). A brief but thoughtful and very readable account of Ratzel's life and a lengthy—even though selective—bibliography.

[7] "Einige Aufgaben einer politischen Ethnographie," *Zeitschrift für Sozialwissenschaft*, Vol. 3 (1900), 1–19; reprinted in *Kleine Schriften von Friedrich Ratzel*, ed. H. Helmolt (Munich and Berlin: R. Oldenbourg, 1906), Vol. 2, Ref. p. 407.

should these two, land and man, be studied in geography? Davis' answer was: In its physical part geography examines all natural features of the earth's surface; in its human part geography considers the effect of these natural features on man and his activities. Here we see clearly presented the dualism that plagued American academic geography from about 1900 to 1930, and that still re-echoes in many of our elementary and secondary schools. This kind of geography, like the old deity Janus, has two faces. One side looks with eyes wide open at the physical earth and tries to understand it without prejudice, drawing freely on any force or process that may explain a valley, mountain, atoll, or coastline. The other face looks at mankind through but one eye, firmly fixed on "nature-man relations," and explains man's behavior as a result of earth's influences, steadfastly ignoring any other factors. In this conception, physical geography studied an *object*, the earth's surface; but human geography by its definition was pledged to look for *relationships* between two objects (earth and man). It was a recipe of two incompatible ingredients. In human geography it led, inevitably, to arguing for the significance of so-called geographic factors rather than to objective research.

The terms "geographic factor" or "geographic influence" are still popular, although they have disappeared from professional literature. They are obviously carry-overs from the early part of this century. Instead, if one wants to indicate a force of the natural environment, he should use such expressions as "physical factors," or more specifically factor of climate, factor of relief, of ground water, etc. After all, "geographic factors" are not merely physical; they include all the circumstances or agents that affect the character of an area.

In North America the two most influential geographers who carried on the study of environmental influences until the middle of this century were Ellsworth Huntington at Yale and Griffith Taylor at the University of Toronto. Both men were stimulating and productive scholars; the former is particularly well known for his many textbooks. At the same time one cannot fail to notice the special pleading for the environmental cause which is the driving force behind their presentations. No one denies the significance of climate, soil, water, or surface features for mankind. However, explaining the variety of human behavior simply through the differentiation of physical environment is a form of sun worship. Instead we need awareness of the subtle interplay of physical and cultural processes which shape the diversity of mankind-on-earth. This conviction gained ground in academic circles in the 1920's and became the dominant view in the 1930's. As is so often the case in the development of the disciplines, geographic education in elementary and

secondary schools continued for a time in the old tracks of environmentalism, unaware that the universities had abandoned them.

In Europe environmentalism found less favor than in the United States.
Already in 1883 Ferdinand von Richthofen proposed a return to the
traditional task of geographers when he insisted that geography must be
a chorological science. *Choros* is the Greek word for place or area.
"Chorography" means place description, and "chorology" the understanding of the interrelations of things and people that give character
to places. Von Richthofen's pupil, Alfred Hettner (1859–1941), gave
further form to this view in his many publications and influenced
American geographers to switch from the study of nature-man relationships to the study of areas.

This is as far as we should go in this historical survey of the field.
It does not mean that there were no important developments in Europe
beyond Hettner or that American geography stood still after rejecting
environmentalism. Rather, the overlapping of recent and of current
thought requires a thematic instead of an historic treatment.

Modern
Viewpoints
in Geography

chapter three

THE HUMANISTIC VIEWPOINT

Before discussing geography as a sober social science we would do well to point out its stake in the humanities. Geographers who want to emulate the exact sciences ignore or even reject this association. But the spirit of the discipline has always been hospitable to art as well as science. We should keep it that way.[1]

The humanities stress real persons and cases rather than models, quality rather than quantity, evaluation and evocation rather than observation, beauty and wisdom rather than information. Geography shares these attitudes to some extent. By tradition it takes a keen interest in the individuality of places, treasures the esthetic values of the landscape, and recognizes that there are more things between heaven and earth than can be safely entrusted to a computer. The humane aspect of geography is especially evident in the way it communicates with the lay audience, including the schools. "Pure" social scientists, among them geographic theoreticians, seem to write only for each other. Their exploration of the frontiers of knowledge may be of vital importance, but there is equal need for discourse with the layman. The general public rightly expects from geography more than some mathematical formulas, framed in a text of studied obscurity. The British scientist

---

[1] There are several stimulating essays on this topic, e.g.: J. K. Wright, "Terrae Incognitae: The Place of Imagination in Geography," *Annals A.A.G.*, 37 (1947), 1–15; S. B. Jones, "The Enjoyment of Geography," *Geographical Review*, 42 (1952), 543–50; Hugh C. Prince, "The Geographical Imagination," *Landscape*, 11 (winter, 1961–62), 22–25; A. H. Clark, "Praemia Geographiae: The Incidental Awards of a Professional Career," *Annals A.A.G.*, 52 (1962), 229–41; J. Leighly, "John Muir's Image of the West," *Annals A.A.G.*, 48 (1958), 309–18. I have borrowed apt phrases from some of these works for this section.

C. P. Snow has written about the two opposing cultures, with the physical scientist at the one pole and the literary intellectual at the other.[2] Something similar exists within the social sciences, causing loss of communication with the laity.

Macaulay spoke of economics as "a dismal science." Some people recall their school geography that way. Apparently the beauty of landscapes, the fascination of discoveries, the confrontation with enigmas, the association of events and places—these and other enrichments of the mind which geography can give—have passed them by. Alexander von Humboldt understood the need for geography to combine science and art. Many of his scientific conclusions have been surpassed, but his vivid descriptions of landscapes, nourished by sensitive and perceptive observation, remain among the best of their kind in geographic literature.[3]

Geography encourages us to observe our surroundings, be it the home town or the whole earth as the home of man. He who has never lived beyond his place of birth accepts the familiar landscape without question. Knowledge of other lands provides the perspective necessary to view one's own. As Kipling said: "What do they know of England who only England know?" Observation, then, is far more than mere seeing. What one sees depends on experience as well as on interest. No two persons, not even two trained geographers, will view a place alike. But each in his own way draws satisfaction from his discoveries.

Through description we share our observations with others. Its substance and form reveal our interest and competence. John K. Wright wrote: "A geographer may portray a place or a region, either with conscientious but unimaginative attention to all details, or with aesthetic imagination in selecting and emphasizing aspects of the region that are distinctive or characteristic. . . If [the geographer] wish his writing and also his teaching to exert their optimum influence, a certain amount of artistry—at least a touch of the aesthetically subjective—must be injected into them."

Meaningful description illuminates important themes and particularizes generalities. It should evoke "the genius of place." In this spirit one should not fear to go across the fence that separates science from literature to pluck imaginative characterizations of place as inspiration for one's own presentation. Hugh Prince writes of an observer of the English landscape around 1800: "In one bold stroke he characterized the old-enclosed district of Norfolk, 'where the eye seems ever on the verge of a forest which is, as it were by enchantment, continually

---

2 *The Two Cultures and the Scientific Revolution* (New York: Cambridge University Press, 1959), 58 pp.

3 See note 2, Chapter 2, p. 15.

changing into enclosures and hedgerows.'" With equal profit and pleasure we may join Freya Stark vicariously on her wanderings through the Middle East, or listen when she reflects on her experiences:

> The pleasure of travel is in this answer of the whole earth, potentially, to our steps, so that every good journey must have in it some measure of exploration, and, if possible, an effort of our own. There is no need to go far; a John Gilpin day is enough: imagination only is needed—and an awareness of the horizon rim beyond which the world is new. And if one were asked which, of all the sights in nature, is most lastingly satisfying, would one not choose the horizon? [4]

Freya Stark expresses so well a sentiment which geographers share that I cannot refrain from quoting her once more:

> Though it may be unessential to the imagination, travel is necessary to an understanding of men. Only with long experience and the opening of his wares on many a beach where his language is not spoken, will the merchant come to know the worth of what he carries, and what is parochial and what is universal in his choice. Such delicate goods as justice, love and honor, courtesy, and indeed all the things we care for, are valid everywhere; but they are variously molded and often differently handled, and sometimes nearly unrecognizable if you meet them in a foreign land; and the art of learning fundamental common values is perhaps the greatest gain of travel to those who wish to live at ease among their fellows. [5]

THE SOCIAL-CULTURAL APPROACH

Geography has always been man-centered. The terms human or anthropo-geography came into use late in the nineteenth century as a reaction to the domination of the field by physical geographers. Even seemingly pure physical studies of climate and relief are, if geographical, related to human notions and values of light, heat, slope, and height. Thus one can say that geography is concerned with the earth as the home of man.

To the environmentalist this meant, as we have seen in Chapter 2, that geography should study how nature conditions or even determines man's behavior. George P. Marsh raised the converse point of man's role in shaping his "home," the earth's surface, though his immediate effect on geographers was apparently small. Friedrich Ratzel recognized

---

[4] *Perseus in the Wind.* By permission of John Murray, Ltd., London. 1956 ed., pp. 154–55.

[5] *Ibid.,* pp. 157–58.

that the spirit and the tools of a people had much to do with their use of the habitat, but his impact was blunted by the environmental views he expressed on other occasions. It remained for Paul Vidal de la Blache (1845–1918), the founder of modern French geography, to define clearly the new goals for geography.[6] Since then his views have been refined and new ideas added, but he deserves our respect for turning, at least in France, the tide of environmental determinism. According to Vidal the earth does not dictate man's behavior. It only offers opportunities; man makes the choice. Here is a quotation from his brilliant volume on France:

> One must start from the notion that a land is a reservoir containing dormant energies of which nature has planted the seed, but whose use depends on man. It is he who, by molding them to his purpose, demonstrates his individuality. Man establishes the connection between disparate elements by substituting a purposeful organization of forces for the incoherent effects of local circumstance. In this manner a region acquires identity and differentiates itself from others, becoming in the course of time like a medal struck in the image of a people.[7]

Because Vidal in rejecting environmental determinism often spoke of "environmental possibilities," his viewpoint has been dubbed "possibilism." However, Vidal did not mean that man is a free agent for whom anything is possible. He recognized fully that man's choice is severely restricted by the value system of his society, its organization, technology, in short, by what Vidal called man's *genre de vie* ("way of life"). The essential truth of this position must be clear to anyone who has reflected on the changes in organization and utilization of space in North America over the last 400 years. The physical environment has not altered substantially, yet successive cultures and forms of economy have put it to very different uses, each of them guided by the purpose as well as the means of the occupying group. For this reason it is meaningless to say that climate is responsible for the citrus fruit farms of Florida and for the skiing resorts of New England. The climate has been the same for a long, long time and is merely a permissive factor; the modern American chooses and acts, though always within the restraints of the social-economic framework.

"Culture" is the modern word for way of life. Anyone interested in more elaborate definitions and their ramifications can consult the anthropologists, for whom culture forms the central theme of their

---

[6] *Principles of Human Geography* (New York: Holt, Rinehart & Winston, Inc., 1926), 511 pp. This is the only one of his works available in English. Most of his essays appeared in the *Annales de Géographie,* which he founded.

[7] *Tableau de la Géographie de la France* (Paris: Hachette, 1903), p. 8.

science. It should, however, be clear by now that culture is also a highly important concept in geographic thought. Each human group—community, society, nation—has its distinctive culture. The study of such groups in their areal differentiation is, strictly speaking, "social geography." This term, although widely used in Europe, never has caught on in the United States. The geographer considers the social group as part of the character of an area. In the United States the distribution of Negroes, Mormons, French Canadians, Amish, Mexicans, and so on, contributes to regional differentiation. In South Asia knowl-

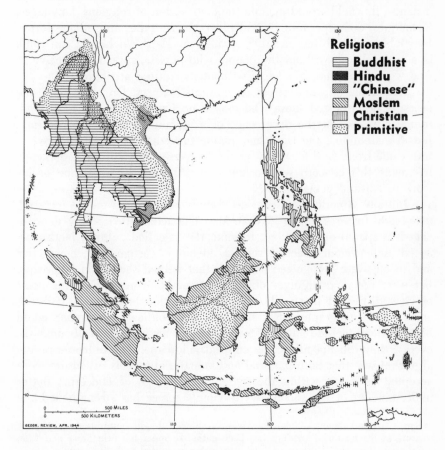

Fig. 1. **Religions in Southeast Asia.** Religions suggest the diversity of cultural influences that have molded Southeast Asia's peoples. What is described in the legend as "Chinese" religion is a mixture of Buddhism, Confucianism, and ancestor worship. From: J. O. M. Broek, "Diversity and Unity in Southeast Asia," *Geographical Review*, 34 (1944), 185, Fig. 6. Map by the author. Reproduced by courtesy of the *Geographical Review*.

edge of the spatial variation of religious and linguistic groups is a prerequisite for understanding the political geography of India, Pakistan, and Ceylon. The diversity and unity in Southeast Asia is largely due to manifold cultural influences which have molded specific social groups (Fig. 1). In the Soviet Union there is a great variety of ethnic groups under the Communist veneer. And who could claim to comprehend Europe without possessing knowledge of nations and national minorities?

If the emphasis is on the cultural traits or complexes themselves rather than the social groups, one should speak of "cultural geography," a term which has gained wide acceptance in the United States. For instance, this field would include the distribution of religions, languages, techniques, domestic animals and plants, house types and village forms. Inevitably cultural and social geography overlap. We hardly can think of a cultural trait without the people who possess, spread, or receive it. And we cannot imagine society without its cultural attributes.

Ratzel placed great stress on cultural features. On more than one occasion he criticized those who looked no further than the local environment to explain the occurrence of a certain trait. On the contrary, Ratzel maintained, the right geographic procedure is to ask where the trait came from. Carl O. Sauer, at the University of California, Berkeley, has made this concern with origin and dispersal a cornerstone of his work in cultural geography.[8]

Initially, American cultural geography concentrated on the material, man-made features which give an area character either singly or associated in spatial arrangement, forming the so-called cultural landscape. Social and economic factors such as ideology, custom, law, commerce, and so on, were recognized as forces that helped shape the landscape, but were not in themselves objects of geographic research. This point of view distressed those who practiced traditional economic, political, and "social" geography. For instance, the political geographer could hardly fail to include national traditions and institutions in his analysis, even if they did not affect the cultural landscape. The outcome of the argument was that both material and immaterial aspects of culture were accepted as being within the geographer's range of concern.[9] Better understanding of the social and economic forces has strengthened the

---

[8] Sauer is the eminent scholar in American historical and cultural geography. A treasure of his masterful writings has been gathered under the title *Land and Life, a Selection from the Writings of Carl Ortwin Sauer,* edited with an introduction by John Leighly (Berkeley, Calif.: University of California Press, 1963), 435 pp.

[9] P. L. Wagner and M. W. Mikesell (eds.), *Readings in Cultural Geography* (Chicago: University of Chicago Press, 1962), 589 pp. A very valuable collection of papers on social-cultural geography by American and foreign geographers.

explanatory description of the "face of the earth."[10] This kind of study has great practical value. The earth as the home of man needs constant reshaping to make it a better place to live. Anyone with some interest in his community realizes how our towns, and especially the fast-growing metropolitan areas, cannot function properly because of defects in their physical layout. Before we can make plans to improve urban and regional land use ("a place for everything and everything in its place"), we need a careful analysis of the present spatial arrangement.

The *social-cultural* point of view, which recognizes man as the active agent, the earth as passive subject, is now generally accepted. It has led some geographers to concentrate on the study of human groups, others to investigate the earth as modified by human action. Whether one argues that geography studies man as inhabitant of the earth, or the earth as the home of man, is mainly a difference of personal inclination. All geographers hold in common a curiosity about places, and "place" includes a piece of land as well as the human group that occupies it.

THE HISTORICAL DIMENSION

A river forms a valley by a series of changes through time, called the process of erosion. Contemplation of "what is where" always leads to the question of why and how it became that way, there. Physical, chemical, and biological processes interact in innumerable combinations. They have formed and continue to form the variety in the earth's natural features. In addition diverse cultural processes have interacted with diverse environments through time, shaping and reshaping the variety of habitats. Present landscapes and societies are like stills from a motion picture. The "here and now" must be understood in the light of the past. Commitments of the present inevitably affect the future. Thus geography, although primarily concerned with arrangements in space, has an historical dimension.

While most geographers agree in principle on this view, they differ considerably in degree of historical treatment. At one extreme stand those who want to maintain the Kantian division between geography and history as much as possible. They insist that geography deals

---

*10 W. L. Thomas, Jr. (ed.), *Man's Role in Changing the Face of the Earth* (An International Symposium under the co-chairmanship of Carl O. Sauer, Marston Bates, and Lewis Mumford [Chicago: University of Chicago Press, 1956]). This massive volume (1193 pp.) contains many excellent papers and summaries of thoughtful discussions on man's impact on the earth.

essentially with the present character of places; therefore, they admit the past only as it is strictly needed to understand the present. For instance, to explain the layout of farms, roads, and cities in coastal California, they would be satisfied with a brief reference to the vast properties bestowed under the Spanish-American land grant system instead of describing the series of subdivisions that have in the course of time led to the present pattern.

At the other extreme are the advocates of "process" as the core of interest. To them the scholar's meat is not so much the explanatory description of the present, but an understanding of the ever changing interplay of forces acting through time which creates the present. Or, they may ignore completely the present and deal with the processes of spatial arrangement and interaction in some past period, more succinctly, with geographic change through time. The injection of the word "geographic" is supposed to distinguish this treatment from history, but the impartial reader may have difficulties in seeing the difference between an historian describing the process of settlement (e.g., W. P. Webb's classic *The Great Plains*) and a geographer tracing "geographic change."[11]

For those who seek a middle ground there is, fortunately, another approach. It is expressed in such terms as "sequent occupance" and "cross-sections through time." Derwent Whittlesey suggested that stages could be recognized during which human occupation of an area remained constant in its fundamental aspects, followed by the onset of rapid and profound changes in the way of life.[12] By analyzing what a place was like in each successive stage the geographer would present a sequent series of "stills." This method, also developed in France and Germany, not only provides insight into the different ways former inhabitants have used the land; it also clarifies the present by pointing out the impact of the past.

Pride and prejudice lead me to sketch the method I used in an historical-geographic study of *The Santa Clara Valley, California*.[13] My main purpose was to understand the changes in the landscape of that valley just south of San Francisco Bay. Here different cultures and phases of economy had rapidly succeeded each other in less than 200 years: The Indian period before the coming of the white man; the Spanish one of missions and cattle ranches in the first half of the nineteenth century; the early American economy of cattle and wheat, lasting

---

[11] For an overview of historical geography emphasizing "process," see A. H. Clark (principal author), "Historical Geography," *American Geography: Inventory and Prospect*, eds. P. E. James and C. F. Jones (Syracuse, N.Y.: Syracuse University Press, 1954), pp. 70–105.

[12] In "Sequent Occupance," *Annals A.A.G.*, 19 (1929), 162–65.

[13] J. O. M. Broek, *The Santa Clara Valley, California: A Study in Landscape Changes* (Utrecht: Oosthoek, 1932), 185 pp.

until the 1870's when the changes began that made the valley into a horticultural district. If the study were done now one would add another phase, the urbanization of the valley, which came largely after the Second World War. Each period until the "present" was a geography of the past. The somewhat original device I used was to divide the treatment of each period in two parts. The first was explanatory: it analyzed the forces and functions that shaped the mode of life in the valley. The second part described the cultural landscape resulting from the social-economic determinants. In this manner, "process" received due attention, but its scope was guided and restrained by the relevance of its forces to the purpose of the study, namely, understanding the landscape. A similar procedure has been adopted for a new historical geography of Great Britain, under the editorship of H. C. Darby, which is to appear before long.

Instead of tracing geographic changes up to the present or seeking the causes of the present back into the past, one can, of course, also concentrate on one distant dateline and inquire what the region was like at that time. H. C. Darby and his associates have done this for eleventh-century England, using the data of the *Domesday Book* as their primary source.[14] Among American studies of this kind special attention should be given to the splendid opus by Ralph H. Brown, *Mirror for Americans: Likeness of the Eastern Seaboard, 1810* (1945). Drawing on all available sources written before that date Brown presented the portrait of the Atlantic coast as seen through the mind of a fictitious geographer of the period. In this manner the author lets us share in the conceptual image which Americans of 1810 had of their habitat. The reader may feel that the author, from the vantage point of present knowledge, could have given more by commenting on erroneous views held in 1810, or by comparing past and present circumstances. Indeed he could, but it would have destroyed the very purpose of the study. The complete immersion in the cultural pattern of another era is no easy feat, but Brown succeeded, producing a classic of historical-geographic scholarship. His textbook on the *Historical Geography of the United States* (1948), more conventional in its treatment, is the best survey of its kind available.

In summary, geography has an historical dimension. Even those geographers who concentrate on the present recognize the genetic aspect: The significance of origin and development of geographic features. How far and in which manner one shall trace the present back into the past depends on the nature of the problem as well as on the

---

14 *The Domesday Geography of Eastern England* (New York: Cambridge University Press, 1952). This was the first volume of an impressive series of which several volumes have since appeared.

interest of the investigator. Historical geography proper deals specifically with the geographic past. Some geographers emphasize process, development, and change, rather than actual description of areas-as-they-were; others use process to explain the character of an area at a cross-section through time.

FACETS OF LOCATION

"Where," as the point of reference, is fundamental to geographic thought. The terms "location," "position," "situation," "site," "distribution," and "arrangement" are the ones most frequently used in geographic literature. They all have to do with the placing of things on the earth's surface. To find where something is requires defining its spatial relationship to known points. To locate is to relate. A ship or plane crossing the ocean determines its position by relating it to the grid of meridians and parallels. If we want to know where Kerguelen Island is we find it by reference to its location at 50° South Latitude and 68° East Longitude. Knowing the mathematical position by means of two co-ordinates is obviously important, like the address on a letter. But it is only the starting point for the discovery of other and more meaningful relationships between a given place and other places.

Relationship between places implies interaction. Interaction requires overcoming distance through communication or transportation, that is, through circulation, to adapt a French term covering all forms of movement. Accessibility measures the degree to which a place is approachable from other places by means of circulation. The evolution of mankind from isolated self-sufficient communities to an interdependent whole means ever more spatial interaction and greater importance of relative location or situation.

In the introductory chapter the terms "site" and "situation" were briefly noted. "Site" as used here means the location of a given place with its local internal features or resources. "Situation" refers to location of a place as related to other places: a place seen in interaction with other places.

An area may be considered as "site" in one case and as "situation" in another. For example, in a study of the spatial relations between the United States and other countries, this country would be the site, the whole earth the situation. In a study on a very large scale the home might be the site, and the urban neighborhood the situation. To understand a place large or small one must evaluate the attributes of its site as well as of its situation.

The environmental determinists placed great emphasis on the internal resources of a country—the site—as if it were an island isolated from external influences. According to their view, dairy farming was determined by cool, humid climate, cotton by a hot and moist growing season. Coastal people became seafarers or remained landlubbers depending on the form of coast. The peoples of northwestern Europe advanced rapidly in civilization because of the cool, variable weather, while the oasis cities of Central Asia fell to ruins because a change in climate dried up their sources of irrigation. In all cases cited we note a disregard of relative location. Dairy farming, for instance, depends first of all on accessibility to markets, that is, situation, rather than being simply a natural response to site advantages. Oasis cities relied for their prosperity on trade routes rather than on local produce from the irrigated fields around them. Thus the decline of Central Asian cities in the late Middle Ages was caused by shifts in trade routes, not climatic change.

The rise of northwestern Europe to paramount status started around 1600. Since there were many causes any explanation in terms of one factor is bound to distort the truth. However, within this complex of factors the favorable situation on the Atlantic seaboard after the Great Discoveries would seem much more important than the stimulating effect—if any—of local climate. The same reasoning should be considered in any attempt to comprehend the rise of the early civilizations in the Middle East. Frequently the explanation stops after pointing out the favorable circumstance of river valleys (Nile, Tigris-Euphrates, Indus) amidst deserts. But there are river flood plains in other desert regions of the world, from the southwestern United States to Australia. Why did these never produce high civilizations? The answer may lie in differences in situation. The Middle East, on the crossroads of continents and sea arms, was an area of interaction for many people. The encounter of men and ideas produced challenges and responses, change, and an open mind to change. Accumulation of innovations meant the rise of civilization.

Central location signifies being accessible to the flows of people, goods, and ideas. It applies to countries and regions, as well as cities. Contrasting with this is marginal location. It is no accident that the southern tips of South America and Africa, as well as Australia and Tasmania, were inhabited until recent times by quite primitive peoples. Living in the world's dead-end streets, they were hardly reached by migrations of peoples and diffusion of new ideas and tools. For similar reasons we see, even in advanced countries, how barriers to movement tend to preserve traditional ways of life, as for instance in the Appalachians, the Scottish Highlands, or in the marshes of Poland and western Russia. "Backwoods" are backward. But a specific situation is not a permanent attribute of place. New routes such as the Panama and Suez canals have created great shifts in locational advantage. Changes in technology of land, sea, and air warfare have affected the strategic value of many an island or land base.

The development of transportation technology has greatly altered the value of the interior of continents. Before the advent of the railroad, long distance mass transport was limited to seas and navigable rivers. The vast mid-latitude grasslands of North and South America, of Asia and Australia, were beyond the pale of Western civilization until the railroad penetrated them a century ago, accompanied by other techniques such as the steel windmill, barbed wire fence, and harvest machine. Since then the automobile and truck, airplane, and various media of communication have further lessened the situational handicaps of these lands. About 1900 the British geographer Halford J. Mackinder, keenly aware of the power of technology to change the value of regions, conceived of an Asian "Heartland" inaccessible to sea power where Russians could build in seclusion a bastion of power from which they eventually would attack the coastal seats of maritime power.[15] The pattern of political power after the Second World War seems to bear out Mackinder's prophecy. A Russian state of continental proportions stands in opposition to the Western sea powers who in turn try to keep Russia out of the oceanic borderlands. In this picture we lose sight, however, of Mackinder's original thesis of the Asian Heartland as the sanctuary of power and undisturbed economic development. Not only have air power and intercontinental missiles destroyed the notion of its inaccessibility, but the Heartland's economic growth remains secondary to that of European Russia. After all, the bulk of Asian Russia is either too cold or too dry for dense settlement. The lesson we must draw from Mackinder's theory is that in evaluating any area we must consider the external relations as well as the internal resources, situation as well as site.

Offhand, it might appear that agricultural land use is little affected by relative location, once the factor of a suitable market is acknowledged. Indeed, the farmer adapts his land use to site conditions of climate, relief, and soils. However, we may have run too quickly past the assumption of the market. Heinrich von Thünen, a German estate owner in the early nineteenth century with great interest in the economics of

---

[15] "The Geographical Pivot of History," *Geographical Journal*, 23 (1904), 421–37. Mackinder elaborated on this theme in his book, *Democratic Ideals and Reality* (New York: Holt, Rinehart & Winston, Inc., 1919; 2d issue, 1942). A shift in his views is apparent in "The Round World and the Winning of the Peace," *Foreign Affairs*, July, 1943, 595–605. Two valuable collections of essays on political geography, many emphasizing location, are: H. W. Weigert and V. Stefansson (eds.), *Compass of the World* (New York: Macmillan, 1944); same editors and R. E. Harrison, *New Compass of the World* (New York: Macmillan, 1949).

farm management, developed a theory—or what we call today a "model"—that is worth our consideration. He assumed a circular, physically homogeneous country, completely isolated from the rest of the world, with only one market at the very center which set the price for all agricultural commodities. Transportation costs in all directions were assumed to increase at the same rate as distance. Thus, with the market price for wheat being the same for every producer, the return to the farmer would depend on how much he had to pay for transportation. To a farmer living nearby the return might be high enough to allow intensive farming, with wheat as one of the rotation crops. A farmer living farther away would get less for his wheat, allowing him to grow only this crop with very little investment of capital or labor. Still farther away, at the very margin of the state, transportation costs to the market would be too high to grow any crops at all. Only goods of high value per unit and collected without great input of labor, such as furs, could stand the cost of transportation. Since transportation cost is the only variable, proportionate to distance in all directions from the central city, the resultant types of land use must form concentric rings, ranging from intensive agriculture close to the city, through extensive farming, to hunting on the margins.[16] This demonstrates that under the given assumptions identical physical environments will be put to very different uses, depending on the distance from the market. Von Thünen's model helps to explain why extensive forms of agriculture prevail—or prevailed until recently—in such distant areas as Argentina, South Africa, and Australia, even where climate and soil conditions match those of the United States or Europe.

The current emphasis in geography on situation counterbalances the former stress on site. This provides for a sounder evaluation unless one now goes to the other extreme and disdains knowledge of local conditions. After all, our concern is with spatial relations between real places, not mere abstract models à la von Thünen. Through human appraisal the properties of the earth become qualities of the human habitat. To comprehend this we need the social-cultural approach, always including the historical perspective. Moreover, in contemplating man's ideas about the quality of places, one must draw upon the humanistic tradition in geography.

---

[16] I have whittled down von Thünen's thesis to the essential point. For more details and references see Hildegard Binder Johnson, "A Note on Thünen's Circles," *Annals A.A.G.*, 52 (1962), 213–20.

Some
Research   chapter four
Themes

On my desk lies a recent issue of the *Geographical Review,* a scholarly journal of international reputation. Its table of contents gives some idea of the topics geographers write about: A new industrial town in Hong Kong, Population potentials for the United States, Soviet subtropical agriculture, Outdoor recreation, Overpopulation in Mauritius, A vegetation map of Tasmania. *Current Geographical Publications,* another periodical of the American Geographical Society, reports the titles of a veritable international torrent of literature. From the many topics we can choose only a few themes as illustrations of the subjects that engage the interest of geographers.

GEOGRAPHIC ASPECTS OF POPULATION

Vidal de la Blache once wrote: "Geography is the study of places, not of men." It was a warning to geographers to keep in mind their main objective, as distinct from that of other social scientists. In geography men are related to the places where they live. In this sense one of the most fundamental questions geography must answer is: "Why are people where they are?"

Distribution

The fundamental fact is the very uneven distribution of population over the earth's surface.[1] This is true of the macroscopic view of the earth as a whole as well as of an area no larger than a township. The

---

[1] There is a large literature on distribution and density of population in the geographical journals. For a broader program formulation see G. T. Trewartha, "A Case for Population Geography," *Annals A.A.G.,* 43 (1953), 71–97.

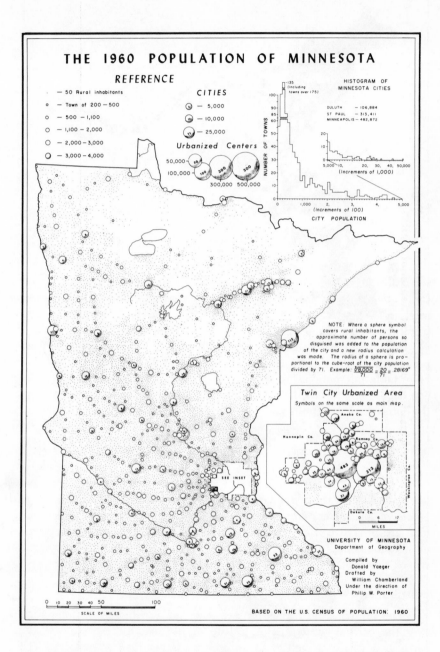

Fig. 2. **Distribution of Population in Minnesota.** Skillful use of dots, circles, and spheres depicts a population pattern that ranges from metropolitan concentration to uninhabited wilderness (however, also see Fig. 3). Courtesy of Professor Philip W. Porter, Department of Geography, University of Minnesota.

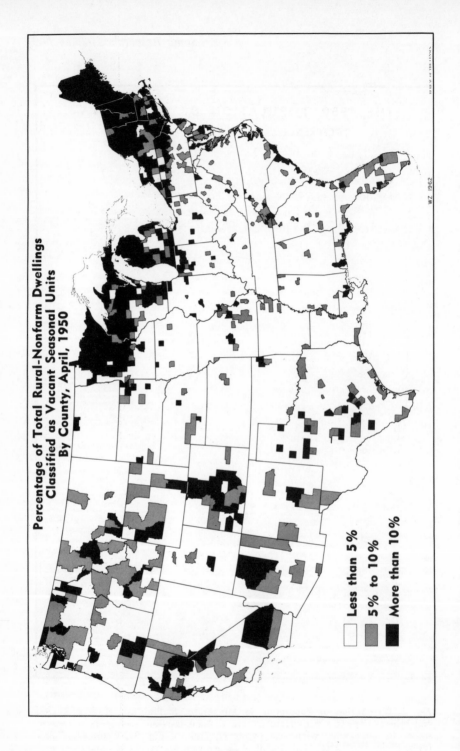

Percentage of Total Rural-Nonfarm Dwellings
Classified as Vacant Seasonal Units
By County, April, 1950

Less than 5%

5% to 10%

More than 10%

WZ 1962

first task, then, is to discover and depict on maps where people live (Fig. 2). More and more countries count their inhabitants by periodic census. The United Nations has an office which aids interested states in improving their census-taking techniques; it publishes world-wide population statistics by countries in its *Demographic Yearbook,* with some comment on the degree of reliability of the data. Population numbers by states are useful information, but they tell us nothing about the distribution within the individual countries. For this, one needs far more detailed figures, if possible by the smallest census units. Still, even these units are arbitrarily defined political or administrative districts (counties, townships) without any relationship to factors that influence the arrangement of population. For instance, a district may comprise a valley and its hilly borders, and its entire population may be concentrated in the valley; the census data do not reveal this. This can be corrected through field observation or map and air-photo interpretation, but these means are not always available.

The census records where people reside, that is, where they sleep, not where they work. Thus the Wall Street district of New York City or the City of London, anthills by day, appear in the census as almost empty areas. More and more people in the United States have a home or cabin for recreational purposes, but are enumerated by the census in the place where they have their main residence. This results in a deceptively low population in, for instance, New England and the northern Great Lakes states, where many people spend their summer and many weekends throughout the year (Fig. 3). Important as enumeration and localization of people are, they serve only as necessary prerequisites for associating distribution with other areal patterns which may explain population arrangement.

Differential Growth of Population

Next to uneven distribution one must consider uneven growth. Discussion of "the population explosion" tends to neglect the specifics of areal variation in the balance of births and deaths. For the geographer differential growth patterns are the meat of demographic data. For many

Fig. 3. **Vacant Seasonal Dwellings in the United States.** The map suggests main areas of rural recreation and retreat. The date of the enumeration (April 1) reflects the situation in regions with cold winter more correctly than that in milder climates. The northern half of the northeastern U.S. is the zone of relatively recent glaciation and hence of attractive recreational opportunities near the great urban zone. From: W. Zelinsky, "Changes in . . . Rural Population . . . ," *Geographical Review,* 52 (1962), 519, Fig. 8. Map by W. Zelinsky. Reproduced by courtesy of the *Geographical Review.*

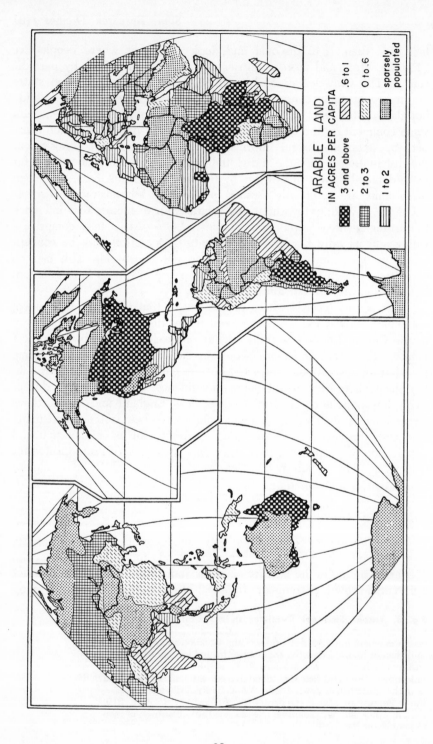

ARABLE LAND
IN ACRES PER CAPITA

3 and above 2 to 3 1 to 2 .6 to 1 0 to .6 sparsely populated

38

countries information is scanty on factors that determine increase, such as annual numbers of births and deaths, age and sex composition, in and out migration. The highly refined techniques of demographers can only be applied to less than half the world's population. In this section we will call attention to the gross patterns of "natural" growth, ignoring effects of migration.

Low fertility and low mortality characterize northwestern Europe and Japan. The populations of these countries increase slowly, less than 1 per cent per year. Moderate fertility and low mortality prevail in Anglo-America, southern South America, South and East Europe including the Soviet Union, Australia, and New Zealand, resulting in an annual increment of around 1.5 per cent. All these countries have commercial-industrial forms of economy and a fair to high level of income. In the so-called underdeveloped countries the introduction of Western science and technology quickly lowers the death rate, but its impact on traditional ways of life, and thus on family size, is much slower. Thus these countries tend to combine high fertility with declining mortality. The fastest rate of growth occurs in those countries that have already attained a low death rate but cling to high birth rates, among them Mexico, Central America, the Caribbean, and some Asian countries, such as Taiwan, the Philippines, Malaya, and Ceylon. Here the annual growth rate lies between 2 and 3, perhaps even 4 per cent per year. Over much of Africa and Asia mortality is still fairly high, but as it declines—and it does—these realms will also attain rapid rates of growth.

In summary, during the next decades underdeveloped countries will grow fast while the developed countries will increase at a slower and decelerating rate. At present the underdeveloped countries contain two-thirds of the world's population of 3,300 million. Judging by current trends, they will in the year 2000 comprise three-fourths of the almost 7,000 million who will then inhabit the earth. It seems reasonable to deduce from experience in Western countries that decreasing fertility will accompany economic progress, leading to slower growth. However, the huge increases in already crowded countries, such as India and China, jeopardize economic progress because the newcomers must be

Fig. 4. Arable Land per Capita. "Arable" land, as defined by the U.N. Food and Agriculture Organization, includes tree crops and fallow and arable land temporarily used for pasture. Note the very low values in East Asia and Northwest Europe. The high values in Central Africa may result from excessive inclusion of fallow land. From: "The Man-Land Ratio," by Jan O. M. Broek, in *The Population Ahead*, edited by Roy G. Francis (Minneapolis: the University of Minnesota Press), p. 56, Fig. 1. Copyright 1958 by the University of Minnesota. Map by the author. Base map copyright by Rand McNally & Co., O.G.S. 906AR.

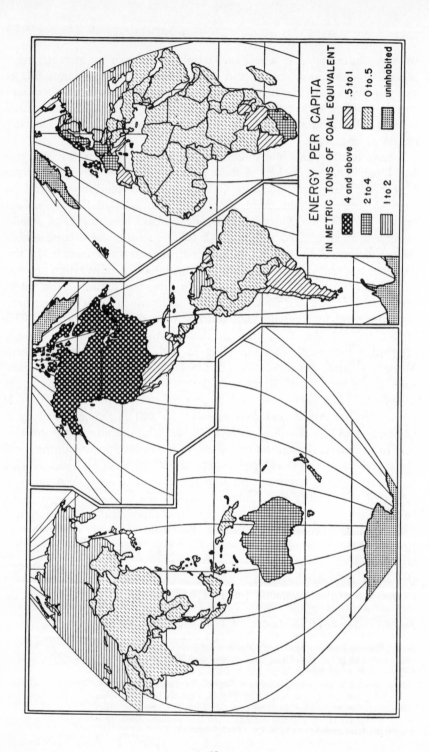

ENERGY PER CAPITA
IN METRIC TONS OF COAL EQUIVALENT

4 and above
2 to 4
1 to 2
.5 to 1
0 to .5
uninhabited

fed, sheltered, clothed, and trained. This leaves little money to invest in building a more productive economy. If this is not a vicious circle, it is at best a spiral road that climbs very slowly towards higher levels of living—along the edge of catastrophe.

Population Density

The most common measurement of density is the mathematical figure arrived at by dividing the number of inhabitants by the number of square miles or kilometers of the district or state in which they live. If applied to large areas it is a very misleading figure because it pays no attention to actual distribution of the population. For instance, Egypt, which is mostly desert, has an average density of only 58 people per square mile, but in the Nile Valley, where Egyptians actually live, the count is about 1,000. To solve this problem various other more refined measures have been proposed, such as the ratio between people and agricultural land.[2] These measures all suffer from trying to put into a simple formula what actually is a very complex relationship. What is "Man" and what is "Land"? Surely, American Man, as a producer and a consumer, is very different from Egyptian Man, not to speak of Papuan Man. Each particular culture acts like a filter through which a people views its habitat. It determines for each society which elements of the land have value—that is, what the resources are. Earth substances become useful only through human appraisal. The iron ore of Minnesota, the water power of Niagara, the uranium of the Congo were useless to the inhabitants until technology and economy discovered their value and found means to exploit them. We call these useful matters "natural resources." Actually they are cultural achievements.[3] Once we understand this we realize how wrong it is to link population density directly

---

[2] J. O. M. Broek, "The Man-Land Ratio," in *The Population Ahead* (Minneapolis, Minn.: University of Minnesota Press, 1958), pp. 52–63. Part of that paper has been adapted for this section.

[3] The classic exposition of the concept of the relativity of resources has been given by E. W. Zimmermann, *Resources and Industries* (New York: Harper & Row, Publishers, 1st ed., 1933; 2d ed., 1951). The first ten chapters, containing the core of the argument, have been republished in paperback as *Erich W. Zimmermann's Introduction to World Resources,* ed. H. L. Hunker (1964).

Fig. 5. Energy Consumption per Capita. "Energy" as used here refers to consumption per capita of commercial sources of power. In contrast to arable land (Fig. 4), energy per capita correlates closely with level of living. From: "The Man-Land Ratio," by Jan O. M. Broek, in *The Population Ahead,* edited by Roy G. Francis (Minneapolis: the University of Minnesota Press), p. 60, Fig. 2. Copyright 1958 by the University of Minnesota. Map by the author. Base map copyright by Rand McNally & Co., O.G.S. 906AR.

with economic well-being.[4] Perhaps as a carry-over from the days when agriculture was the mainstay of life, we still believe that teeming millions crowded in space spell poverty: the less arable land there is per inhabitant, the lower the level of living.

Let us look at the facts (Fig. 4). China, Korea, Japan, the Philippines, and Ceylon have less than ½ acre of arable land per capita. The same is true in the Caribbean for Haiti, Puerto Rico, and Jamaica. At the other extreme are the United States with 3 acres of arable land per capita, Canada with twice as much, and Australia in between the two (pastures have been omitted). This contrast between poor and rich countries seems to prove the point. But a glance at western Europe shatters the naive hypothesis. Here are several countries with less than ½ acre of arable land per inhabitant: Great Britain, the Low Countries, West Germany, and Switzerland. Their neighbors have not much more. In material wealth they certainly are upper middle class when compared to the countries mentioned in Asia and the Caribbean. In short, whatever the values of various man-land ratios may be, they fail as reliable yardsticks to measure wealth or poverty (Fig. 5).

In the same vein we must guard against the glib use of the term "overpopulation." The common notion behind this concept seems to be that people are merely consumers who must divide a static amount of "resources." But people are also producers. More applied science and more tools can increase resources and productivity. No one yet has found the correct universal formula to define "optimum population," from which to measure what is over- and what is underpopulation. What is "optimum," or best, involves value judgments on what is "the good life" materially as well as spiritually. We do not intend to argue away the real problems posed by increasing population. To the contrary, the point is that they are recognized more easily if we do not first cover them up by the undefinable word "overpopulation."

Population Movements

Births and deaths determine the size of the earth's population. For the growth or decline of individual countries or districts one must also consider in and out migration. From 1600 to the early twentieth century Europeans left their homelands in increasing numbers for the "new" lands overseas. But that period of voluntary mass migration is over. Instead we have witnessed forced mass expulsions. Even those countries which are still eager for immigrants have a very selective admission

---

[4] This statement refers to present regional differences. However, if the world population were to grow everywhere to "standing room only" (a situation that would arise if present trends were to continue) there would be indeed a causal link between density and poverty.

policy. This means that emigration as the safety valve for population pressure is out. Barring war and new forced displacements, the people of each state must make the best of it at home.

The larger countries have vast stretches which are virtually empty. But people do not move toward space; they move toward better opportunities. The best lands are occupied. Opening up new frontiers for agriculture requires special skill and great outlay of capital, both of which may yield better returns by intensifying cultivation on existing farms. There is no reason to believe that the cold lands, the deserts, and the equatorial forests offer ready outlets for surplus population—at least not in the present state of our knowledge. Thus the internal migrations in search for the better life are mainly movements within the *ecumene,* the inhabited world. In the first half of this century millions of Chinese have pushed into Manchuria. Russians settled beyond the Urals in large numbers, whether voluntarily or otherwise. In the United States many have gone West, particularly to California, during the decades since the war. In Europe, too, almost every country has experienced regional changes in population. However, the largest internal migration going on all over the world is the shift from the country and small towns to the cities (see below).

"Migration" is mass movement from one region or country to another for the purpose of permanent settlement. There are, of course, many other kinds of movement, all of which receive attention in the geographic literature. Among them are pastoral nomadism, "transhumance" (the long distance seasonal movement of livestock accompanied, in contrast to nomadism, by only a few shepherds), seasonal travel by harvest laborers, the spring floods of vacationers, and the massive daily tides of commuters between home and work.

URBAN GEOGRAPHY

We live in a time of rapid technical, economic, and social change. Farming, mining, and even manufacturing, require less and less manpower, while the so-called tertiary industries, or the service sector of the economy, need more and more workers. Ever greater numbers gather in large urban communities. At the same time the structure of the city itself undergoes drastic transformation. Urban geography brings into clear focus the concepts of location, interaction, circulation, and accessibility, as well as distribution and movements of population.[5]

---

[5] H. M. Mayer and C. F. Kohn (eds.), *Readings in Urban Geography* (Chicago: University of Chicago Press, 1959), 625 pp. This volume contains a fine collection of articles dealing with various aspects of the field.

What Is a City?

To define the city in the terms of its incorporation proves unsatisfactory under present conditions of urban sprawl. Nor is high population density a good criterion for definition, because many American suburbs have fewer people per square mile than do farming areas in China. Size of population sounds like a good measure until we try to define the lower limit. The U.S. Census draws the line between rural and urban at incorporated places of 2,500 inhabitants, but other countries set different limits. The more satisfactory definition of the city is by function. In essence the urban community performs centralized services for its surrounding area. The U.S. Census recognizes this in its definition of the "Standard Metropolitan Area": besides the county which contains a city of at least 50,000 people, other contiguous counties are included if according to certain criteria they are essentially metropolitan in character and socially and economically integrated with the central city.

The area which is related to the city is variously called "trade area," "sphere of influence," "hinterland" (especially for ports), "umland," "supporting and tributary area." How far the influence of a city reaches can be measured by the spatial extent of travel, long distance telephone connections, newspaper circulation, wholesale deliveries, and so on. At best there is only a rough coincidence of the limits of each function. Usually one can distinguish an inner zone which is intimately linked to the city and an outer zone where influences of two or more cities overlap.

Cities can be distinguished according to their predominant function, such as that of commerce, administration, transportation, manufacturing, and social-cultural services (e.g., education, recreation, medical center). Most cities combine two or more functions. The census provides statistical data to recognize and measure the functions of cities, among them employment figures for various industries and services.

One should not regard the studies of functions and spheres of influence as mere academic diversions. They attempt to find out what makes a city tick. Merchants in small trade centers know all too well that their existence, and that of the whole town, hinges on the farmers of the surrounding trade area. As the farming population shrinks, so does the town, unless it adds new functions or broadens its sphere of influence. The same applies, in principle, to any city's rate of growth or decline. Thus urban places exist by earning income through the sale of centralized services. This statement needs, however, some refinement. Even in a small town there are people who earn their living by serving exclusively the townsfolk, say a boardinghouse or the street repair crew. The larger the city the greater the proportion of inhabitants who exist by "taking in each other's washing." One must, therefore, distinguish between business and industry which really earn income from the outside—the so-called basic or external functions—and the ancillary, nonbasic or internal functions.

Central Place Theory

The distribution of cities as central places has been clarified in recent years by the concept of spatial hierarchy.[6] Let us begin with the small town. It provides for its immediate surroundings services of daily convenience, the kind of things a frontier farmer would have done for himself. There are grocery, drug, hardware, general merchandise stores, and a bank. Towns of this rank are necessarily closely spaced. Central places of the next order are larger and have a wider range of more specialized retail services, including clothing, shoe, furniture stores, lumber yard, hotel, mortuary, and so on. Since these types of business require substantial numbers of customers to sustain them, the towns lie farther apart and comprise within their supporting area a number of lower order (daily convenience) centers. The next higher order of cities is characterized by the wholesale function they perform for the two lower orders. Still higher in the spatial hierarchy stand the regional headquarters, with commodity exchanges, insurance offices, large department stores and mail order houses, and convention hotels. At the top of the pyramid are cities like New York, London, and Paris which act as national hubs. These cities and others, such as Hong Kong, Singapore, and Zürich, are also among the ranking seats of trade and finance in the international hierarchy.

One can make, of course, a similar hierarchy for government or school systems, always going from the simple to the complex, from small to large, each unit differentiated as well as integrated by the specific tasks it performs within the whole. It will be noted that manufacturing industries oriented toward raw materials or power do not fit into such a scheme. Nor do mining, fishing, and resort towns because of their linkage to specific sites. Moreover—and this applies to central places as well as towns with other functions—the legacy of the past has considerable effect on the actual spacing of urban places (Fig. 6). Only in an entirely new country can one arrange service centers in such manner that they reflect present circulation, technology, and consumer prefer-

---

[6] The German geographer Walter Christaller developed the theory that under certain given conditions towns would develop in the center of the area they served and at stated distances from each other. He replaced the circular areas by hexagons to avoid overlapping of the circles. A hierarchy of centers would develop in this hexagonal framework (*Die zentralen Orte in Süddeutschland* [Jena: Gustav Fischer, 1933]). See also discussions in textbooks such as R. Murphey, *An Introduction to Geography* (Chicago: Rand McNally & Co., 1961), 699 pp.; and J. W. Alexander, *Economic Geography* (Englewood Cliffs, N.J.: Prentice-Hall, Inc., 1963), 661 pp.

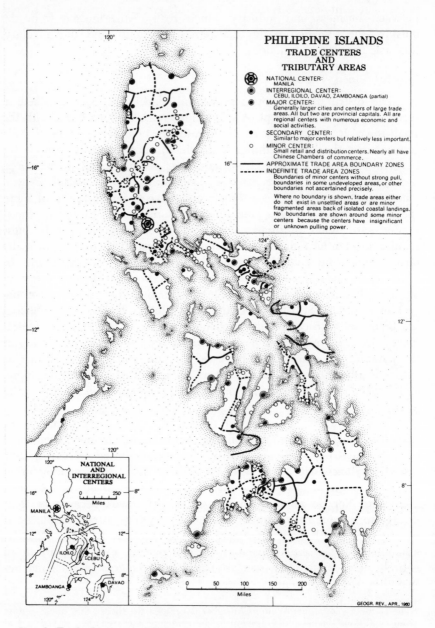

Fig. 6. Trade Centers and Tributary Areas, the Philippines. This map also shows the rank in the hierarchy of trade centers. The arrangement and structure reflect the island nature of the Republic and the highland barriers within the islands, as well as historical factors. From: E. L. Ullman, "Trade Centers and Tributary Areas of the Philippines," *Geographical Review*, 50 (1960), 208, Fig. 3. Map by E. L. Ullman. Reproduced by courtesy of the *Geographical Review*.

encès. The Dutch have done this in the lands newly reclaimed from the sea. Even so, in the light of increasing motorization, they have placed service centers too closely together.

Situation and Site

The general theory of spatial hierarchy gives perspective to the location of the individual city. Location has, as explained before, two aspects: situation and site. The former accounts in a general way for the existence of an urban center in a favorable area; the latter is the specific spot where the city stands. For instance, after the European colonization of North America, the seaboard of the Mohawk-Hudson corridor and the San Francisco Bay region provided superb geographic situations for the development of great ports. But what were the circumstances that led to the choice of Manhattan island rather than Long Island or the New Jersey shore, and the narrow hilly peninsula at the Golden Gate rather than the east side of the bay or up the Sacramento River? These questions can only be answered by understanding the local topography as the early settlers perceived it in the context of their needs and aims.

The momentum of an early start has usually kept a city on approximately the same site. Sometimes the early site was vacated for a better spot, as, for example, in Minneapolis-St. Paul. There the original fur trading settlement, under the protection of strategically located Fort Snelling, was abandoned in favor of the river crossing and the water power of the rapids upriver (Minneapolis) and the steamboat landing downstream (St. Paul). Locating new capitals requires careful consideration of both situation and site, and provides geographers with interesting case studies such as Canberra (Australia) and Brasilia.

Internal Structure

The closer (larger scale) view concerns itself with the layout or plan (the anatomy) as well as the functional activities (the physiology) within the city.

Most Americans are so used to the grid pattern of streets and city blocks that they think of it as the natural, universal plan for cities. Actually it is a special device, an invention which from its probable origin in the Middle East spread to Greece and then throughout the Roman Empire. Its use implies forethought; its enforcement requires central authority. It is no wonder that the grid plan was virtually forgotten in the feudal Middle Ages. It was rediscovered in the Renaissance, and the Spanish government insisted on its use for the new cities established in its American domain. In the United States the grid was apparently first used for Charleston, South Carolina, in 1680, soon to be followed by Philadelphia (1682). The rectangular Range and Township Survey came a century later (1785) and reinforced the use of the grid. Since it is far from perfect for all purposes, it is being replaced in modern city planning by other designs.

Transportation and communication technology is the great force modifying the urban functional structure. The large city of some fifty years ago had its central business district (the "CBD" as it is now called in professional parlance) tightly grouped near the railroad station. Radial streetcar lines connected it with the residential areas. Railroads leading into the city had small suburbs at their local stations. Except for minimum daily conveniences, everyone shopped "downtown." Altogether, the technology of circulation favored strong concentration, with intense localization of functions. Modern development, however, permits more decentralized patterns. In other words, centrifugal forces rather than centripetal ones appear now to have the upper hand.

Circulation bridges distance but does not eliminate it. Thus there always remain advantages to proximity; only the notion of what is near and what is far, and for what purpose, changes. Modern ease and speed of circulation, therefore, do not mean that any establishment can locate anywhere in the urban area. They mean that functions are regrouped according to current means and ends. Suburbs have filled the interstices between the railroad stations; shopping centers have followed the customers to their new locations. Not only people but also jobs are moving to the suburbs. Many manufacturing industries and some types of administrative offices have fled the congested and high-rent areas near or in the CBD to settle in one-story buildings located in pleasant surroundings on the outskirts of the city.

This transformation from tightly nucleated city to metropolitan sprawl is familiar to everyone. To measure the changes and comprehend the processes require detailed research, in which many geographers participate. What is happening to the CBD, or even the whole central city of a metropolitan area? In the city of 1900 the arrangement of functions and related land use presented somewhat concentric rings of decreasing intensity from center to periphery, reminding one of von Thünen's circles. Now the question is: Will the center retain the essence of urban substance or become the hole in the doughnut? It is likely that after the sorting-out process is over the old hub will prove its value for certain functions that require the highest degree of centrality, and even may attract new residents who prefer its central location.

Another line of research examines the spread of urbanization on the periphery of the city in "exurbia" and "interurbia." Here deceptively rural landscapes are actually occupied by people who have their work in the city or perform essentially urban services. This "rurban" periphery is particularly noticeable in the huge urban belt from Boston to Washington, D.C. This is "Megalopolis, the Main Street of the Nation," of which the geographer Jean Gottmann has given us a thoughtful analysis.[7] Similar urban regions stretch between Pittsburgh and Cleveland, Chicago and Milwaukee, around San Francisco Bay and Los Angeles. In western Europe a huge urbanized area is growing between the Rhine delta and northern France, reaching eastward into central Germany and southward along the Rhine to Frankfort. Other examples are southern England and southern Japan from Tokyo west to Kobe-Osaka.

Although urbanization is occurring all over the earth, one must beware of transferring generalizations for American cities to countries with different cultures and economies. For instance, Indian cities so far maintain a compact character. In contrast to the United States, where the rich live in the suburbs and the poor in the "grey belt" surrounding the CBD, in India the rich prefer residence in the center while the poor are packed tightly together in the outskirts. We need more intensive studies of urban places in other parts of the world before we can make meaningful comparisons.

THE WORLD IN ORDER

To the examples of topical inquiry one could easily add many more, such as the geography of agriculture, manufacturing industries, land forms, and vegetation. Instead, we will review briefly some attempts to divide the earth into broad regions. Each of such divisions is based on the notion that some feature, be it simple or complex, provides a significant clue for understanding the world around us. Each era and each culture reinterprets and redivides the world according to its own knowledge and outlook. But often the old image discarded by science lives on in the folklore.

Climatic Divisions

A good example of a geographic myth is the popular belief in Frigid, Torrid, and Temperate Zones, as originally developed by the ancient Greeks. It was essentially a division of the earth according to exposure to sun rays. It failed to take into account the differential heating of land and water, air currents, altitude, and cloud cover, all of which cause considerable deviations of temperature within each zone of insolation. And, of course, it completely ignored the equally critical item of precipitation. Modern climatic systems are based on

---

[7] *Megalopolis, the Urbanized Northeastern Seaboard of the United States* (New York: Twentieth Century Fund, 1961), 810 pp.

actual temperature as well as precipitation, or—and better—on temperature and available moisture, bearing in mind the loss of water through
evaporation and through transpiration from plants. In spite of a hundred
years of progress in understanding climates, the simple notion of heat
zones lingers on. Until 1941 the U.S. Quartermaster provided three
standard issues of military clothing and equipment for latitudinal zones
labeled Temperate, Torrid, and Frigid.

Because the current climatic classifications reflect the various biologic
environments, they have value in offering an orderly view of the earth
as the home of man. A number of textbooks and a far greater number of
courses use climatic regions as the basic segments of the earth. Environmental determinism being a thing of the past, one may assume that
climate is merely considered as the natural setting for human action.
The question remains whether it is the most suitable framework.

Continents

Another item in the folklore of geographic thought is the importance
which many people attach to continents as basic divisions of the earth.
If we recognize them for what they are—concepts of the human mind,
convenient handles, instead of units ordained by nature—we can alter
or ignore them to fit our needs. Surely, it is nothing else than convention
to call Australia a continent and Greenland a large island. We usually
consider North and South America as two continents bisected at the
Isthmus of Panama. Geologic history gives this some justification, but
human history denies it. The isthmus has served as a zone of migration
and cultural diffusion rather than a barrier.

The Old World traditionally is divided into Europe, Asia, and
Africa. This goes back to the Greek conception of the *ecumene* and its
parts.[8] At one time, in the sixth century B.C., "Asia" comprised all
lands south of the Mediterranean–Black Sea–Caucasus–Himalayas, and
"Europe" all to the north of this "parallel"—one of those neat symmetri-
cal partitions the Greeks loved. A century later there appeared another
order in which the axis had shifted from west-east to north-south:
"Lybia" (the later Africa) was cut off from Asia, the dividing line variously placed at the western border of Egypt, the Nile, or the Red Sea.
"Europe" lay north of it and stretched east as far as the Don River in
southern Russia. Opposite these two western quadrants spread "Asia"
as the eastern half of the known world. What thought underlay this
arrangement? Surely not the search for major natural boundaries. Rather,
it reflected the Greek awareness of cultural differences. Natural features

[8] F. Lukermann, "Asia, Libya, Europe: Place and Idea." I thank the author for his
courtesy in letting me read the full text of his paper, an abstract of which appeared
in *Annals A.A.G.*, 52 (1962), 348.

only served as physical markers for the approximate boundaries. For the same reason the eastern boundary of "Europe" later shifted to the Urals. Does this line suit our modern world view? The Soviet Union extends over eastern Europe and northern Asia. To treat part of it as "Europe" and part as "Asia" does not make much sense. Yet, it goes against the historic grain to include the entire Soviet empire in "Europe." More and more a noncommittal threefold division is being used, as in the publications of the United Nations: Europe, the Soviet Union, and Asia.

Hemispheres

The "Western Hemisphere" presents a similar tangle of physical and cultural—in this case especially political—notions. Much has been written about hemisphere solidarity, hemisphere defense, etc., but few people bother to find out what the Western Hemisphere really contains. Taking the meridian of 20° West Longitude as its conventional though arbitrary eastern limit, then the western boundary falls, by definition, 180 degrees west, at 160° East Longitude. A glance at the map shows that this hemisphere includes not only the Americas and almost all of Greenland but also a substantial chunk of Soviet northeastern Asia as well as New Zealand. If this covers more ground and water than intended, we had better abandon the term Western Hemisphere and speak instead of the American quarter sphere, or simply "The Americas." But even in this more restricted frame of reference "the myth of the continents" has long held us in its grip. Eugene Staley wrote an article under that title in 1941 in which he effectively demonstrated the fallacy of conceiving a physical land mass as the "natural" entity for economic, political, and strategic unity.[9] In direct line (great circle distance) Buenos Aires, Argentina, is farther from Chicago than any capital in Europe, including Moscow. Is Argentina more vital for U.S. defense than any part of Europe because it happens to be connected by land with the United States? This question is not to suggest national policy but to point up the danger of simplistic reasoning based on continental concepts.

The psychological isolationism in the United States resulted in part from misconceptions fostered by the Mercator world map and similar projections which center on the equatorial zone and present the land masses as arranged from east to west, separated by wide ocean moats running north-south. A look at the globe or at a map projection centered on the North Pole shows that actually North America and Eurasia cluster tightly around the Arctic midland sea.

---

[9] "The Myth of the Continents," *Foreign Affairs*, April, 1941; republished in revised form in *Compass of the World* (1944), pp. 89–108.

Instead of bisecting the globe into a Western and an Eastern Hemisphere we may split it into halves in such a manner that one half has the greatest possible amount of land. It will be found that this "Land Hemisphere" has its pole near Nantes, northwestern France (Fig. 7).

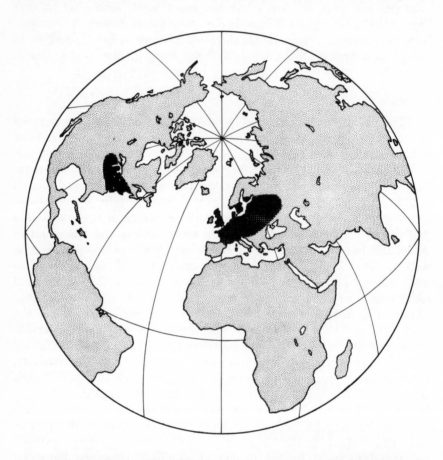

Fig. 7. The Land Hemisphere. The so-called Land or Principal Hemisphere has its pole in northwestern France. The dark-shaded areas on both sides of the Atlantic form the world's main industrial-commercial zone. Adapted from J. Parker Van Zandt, *The Geography of World Air Transport* (1944). Reproduced by courtesy of the Brookings Institution.

Only southern South America, part of Southeast Asia, Australia, and New Zealand lie in the "Water Hemisphere." The land, or principal hemisphere, contains 81 per cent of the total land surface (90 per cent if one excludes Antarctica), 95 per cent of the world's population, and generally over 90 per cent of all economic production. Inside this land hemisphere lies the industrial core of the earth, stretching from the eastern United States through Central Europe into Russia, with four-fifths of all factory output, and nine-tenths of all coal and steel production. This view brings out proximity. Distance has meaning even in a "shrinking world." As geographers we never deal with abstract mathematical space but always with properties of filled space. That is why the division into water and land hemispheres adds to the understanding of concrete spatial reality.

Political and Economic Divisions

Halford J. Mackinder sketched a division of the earth that has fascinated geographers as well as statesmen (Chapter 3). In essence it rested on the relations between form of mobility and geographic situation. In his view the Heartland, inaccessible to sea power, was surrounded by the "Inner Crescent," that is, the oceanic rimlands of Eurasia. Farther distant lay the countries of the "Outer Crescent" such as the Americas and Australia. The error of conceiving North America as "distant" from Eurasia could only arise from contemplating a Mercator map, and before the advent of air power. Mackinder later altered his world view. Whether one agrees or disagrees with him, there is no denying that his thesis was a bold and stimulating attempt to reduce the turbulent world to order.[10]

Economic geography has used various systems to distinguish major world regions. That economic regions should be organized by economic criteria seems obvious until one recalls textbooks and courses in economic geography which are arranged by climatic regions. More justifiable is the division of the earth according to predominant economic activities, such as agriculture, mining, fishing, and manufacturing, and further distinguished by commercial and subsistence purposes.

The current trend views all economic activities of a country as an interrelated complex and measures its level of development by such indices as per capita power use, food consumption, income, and the proportion of workers in the various sectors of economic activity. In this manner all countries of the world can be compared in regard to material well-being. When we transfer the list to a world map we soon discover a distinct areal pattern of "haves" and "have-nots." The countries most advanced in level of living are the United States, Canada, Australia, and New Zealand, followed by Europe, including the Soviet Union. The only country in Asia that would qualify for this group, except for its lower income per capita, is Japan. At the other extreme are most

---

*10 For other aspects of political geography see the collection of essays in W. A. Douglas Jackson (ed.), *Politics and Geographic Relationships* (Englewood Cliffs, N.J.: Prentice-Hall, Inc., 1964), 411 pp.

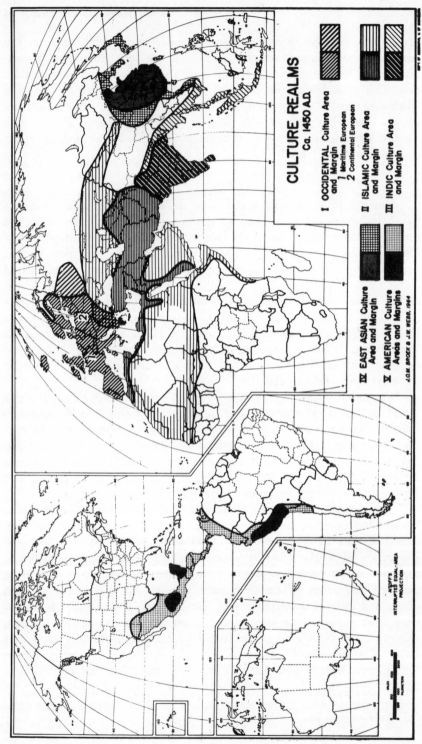

CULTURE REALMS
Ca. 1450 A.D.

I OCCIDENTAL Culture Area
and Margin
1 Maritime European
2 Continental European

II ISLAMIC Culture Area
and Margin

III INDIC Culture Area
and Margin

IV EAST ASIAN Culture
Area and Margin

V AMERICAN Culture
Areas and Margins

J.O.M. BROEK & J.W. WEBB, 1964

HOFF'S
INTERRUPTED EQUAL-AREA
PROJECTION

MILES

of Asia's rimlands, Africa, and the equatorial parts of South America. Differences in economic levels relate in many ways to social characteristics. Low level of income, as a rule, is accompanied by prevalence of illiteracy, disease, poor housing, high proportion of rural population, and high fertility.

Understanding the spatial pattern of various forms and levels of living is of paramount importance in an era deeply concerned with the differential economic growth of nations. One should be on guard, however, against the danger of conceiving the economic process as something quite separate from the social-cultural environment. The financial aid given to western Europe under the Marshall Plan produced excellent and almost immediate results because it was injected into a society geared to industrial-commercial production. A similar sum poured into an underdeveloped area would be largely wasted because the society would not be ready to use it productively. Economic development must go hand in hand with social change.

Culture Realms

Since the economy of a people is closely interwoven with value systems, traditions, and social organization, in short, with its culture, there is great merit in arranging the world by cultural regions. The thought is by no means new. The Greeks had it in mind when they distinguished Europe from Asia and Africa. In modern geography it has gained strength with the application of culture to geographic problems. Research must necessarily restrict itself to the step-by-step investigation of special topics or of areas rather limited in size, but for the purposes of exposition one may leap forward and employ a provisional partition of the earth into broad culture realms. Various writers in Europe and in the United States have proposed their individual schemes. All are much alike. In essence, they distinguish the following realms: Occidental or Western; Islamic or North African–Southwest Asian; Indic or Indian; East Asian or Oriental; Southeast Asian; Meso–African or Negro–African. The Occidental realm may be further divided into the European cradle land, its overseas wings of Anglo– and Latin America, South Africa, Australia, and New Zealand, and its eastern continental wing, the Soviet Union (Figs. 8 and 9).

Fig. 8. Culture Realms about A.D. 1450. In the Old World the belt of higher civilizations stretched from Atlantic to Pacific; in the Americas it ranged from Mexico to Peru. Note the modest area of Occidental culture before the European eruption. Copyright J. O. M. Broek and J. W. Webb.

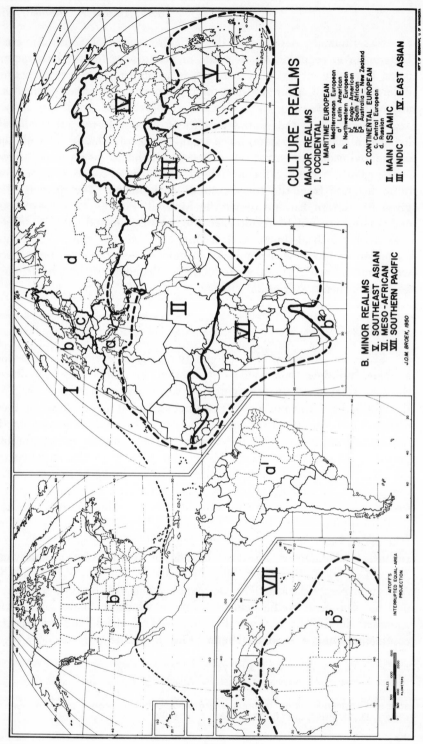

CULTURE REALMS

A. MAJOR REALMS
  I. OCCIDENTAL
    1. MARITIME EUROPEAN
      I. Latin American
        a¹ Latin American
      b. Northwestern European
        b¹ Anglo-American
        b² South African
        b³ Australia-New Zealand
    2. CONTINENTAL EUROPEAN
      c. Central European
      d. Russian
  II. MAIN ISLAMIC
  III. INDIC   IV. EAST ASIAN

B. MINOR REALMS
  V. SOUTHEAST ASIAN
  VI. MESO-AFRICAN
  VII. SOUTHERN PACIFIC

J.O.M. BROEK, 1950

AITOFF'S
INTERRUPTED EQUAL-AREA
PROJECTION

These realms are individuals of a higher order than nations. Just as a nation has grown historically into an entity in which the people are bound together by a common ideology, so a culture realm is a composite of peoples who share the legacy of the past and general attitudes. Admittedly, the essence of a culture is not easy to grasp, let alone measure, and boundaries between culture realms are rarely sharp lines. But who would deny that within the unity of mankind profound differences exist between the ways of thinking, feeling, and believing in the United States, Nigeria, Iran, and Korea? In Malaya one can not fail to notice the contrasts between the competitive, industrious Chinese and the easy-going Malays. The terms "Anglo–America" and "Latin America" are meaningful in suggesting, however vaguely, differences in value systems. Culture realms give us perspective on the diversity of mankind. We approach them with respect born from the understanding that they are historical personalities, not merely to be measured by their economic status in comparison with the United States. The impact of Occidental culture on other realms is profound, but the changes now in progress are not likely to lead to a world-wide homogenized civilization, modeled after the Occident. Each non-Western culture will mold the foreign intrusions in its own image. The world will be more interdependent, more of a unity, but will not lack cultural diversity.

Fig 9. **Culture Realms about A.D. 1950.** Occidental culture has affected but not replaced the other major Old World cultures (compare Fig. 8) nor some of the minor culture realms in the tropics. The scale does not allow detail, such as scattered remains of American Indian culture areas. Designed by the author in 1950. Copyright J. O. M. Broek.

<h1>The Methods of Geography</h1>

chapter five

Geography shares with the other social sciences a number of methods, but there is one which is so inherently geographic that it deserves attention above all others. This is the regional approach. Its employment requires the use of cartographic techniques, sometimes also called the cartographic method. This chapter will review briefly the regional method and the use of maps, with an interlude on quantitative techniques.

THE REGIONAL METHOD

The dualism in geography as stated by Varenius (p. 13) concerned the contrast between general (systematic, now more often called topical) geography and special (regional) geography. Topical geography investigates, as James puts it, "a particular group of features produced by one kind of process wherever these features may occur in the world." [1] Regional geography has its focus on a specific area which has some kind of homogeneity, resulting from the association of areally related features. This apparent dualism, however, resolves itself if we consider the topical and regional aspects as two applications of the regional method.

For instance, if we are interested in the topic of location of manufacturing industries, we look for regions of the world that are homogeneous in terms of this specific criterion. In turn, when we prac-

---

[1] P. E. James, "American Geography at Mid-Century," in *New Viewpoints in Geography*, Twenty-ninth Yearbook of the National Council for the Social Studies, ed. P. E. James (Washington, D.C.: NCSS, 1959), p. 10.

tice so-called regional geography we select certain features (topics) as criteria for marking out the region. After all, every spot on the earth is unique and full of diverse things. It is futile to think that one can master the totality of content of any area. To handle the areal complexity, to see the forest instead of the trees, we must ignore irrelevant details and grasp the dominant features that characterize the area. Inevitably, this means that one defines the region by some selected features. A region, then, is an area homogeneous in terms of the specific criteria chosen to delimit it from other regions.

Anyone who compares the regional divisions of the United States or of the earth in various textbooks can see how different authors, starting from different premises and using yardsticks appropriate to their objectives, have come up with a variety of regions. He who believes that land forms are the major lineaments to which man must ultimately conform will divide the United States by major relief features; others use climate or main economic activities. Still others define each individual region by whatever feature seems to hold the key to understanding its singular character. Thus, the delimitation of a region is always based on a mental judgment. The recognition of regions as products of the mind contrasts sharply with the old notion that regions existed in nature as objective facts which science, if it looked hard enough for the laws of nature, could discover like the table of chemical elements.

Rather than a defeat, this modern recognition of the region as an intellectual concept signified a gain because it overcame the old dualism between "topical" and "regional" studies. Both use the regional method for understanding the areal differentiation of the earth. "The study of a topical field in geography involves the identification of areas of homogeneity, which is the regional approach; the study of regions that are homogeneous in terms of specific criteria makes use of the topical approach, because the defining criteria are topical." [2]

Although the regional method is common to both approaches, the procedures and results may be quite different. In a regional study one starts with the hypothesis that the area is a region and then examines its components and connections. In light of the knowledge gained, one confirms or revises the initial boundaries and interprets the "personality" of the region. Throughout the procedure the guiding idea is to provide a synthesis of the region as a complex association of features. The topical approach starts with a question, such as: Where are the flour mills in the United States, and why are they there? The regional patterns of the

[2] D. Whittlesey (principal author), "The Regional Concept and the Regional Method," *American Geography: Inventory and Prospect*, eds. P. E. James and C. F. Jones (Syracuse, N.Y.: Syracuse University Press, 1954), p. 31.

flour mills and of all other features that seem relevant to the problem are then examined and compared. The procedure is essentially analytical.

The previous chapters contain numerous examples of topical regions. It will suffice to summarize the main categories. The most common and best known are regions based on one or more uniform features or feature complexes, such as climatic or economic regions. Such areas of homogeneity are often called uniform or formal regions. Another category of regions, which receives increasing attention, emphasizes homogeneity in internal structure or functional organization as, for instance, the trade area of a city. Such regions are designated as functional or nodal ("nodal" because they usually have a center or node to which the region is tied by internal circulation).

Regions are not of any set size. They range from localities no larger than a little valley or a small trading area to realms as vast as Latin America or Southeast Asia. Small regions may be combined into larger ones or large ones broken down into smaller units. Obviously the degree of generalization will differ according to the scale of the investigation.

QUANTITATIVE TECHNIQUES

In geography, as in all other social sciences, there is much discussion of the need to develop quantitative methods. The terminology is unfortunate because it gives the impression that geography was not interested in the exact measuring of quantities until a few years ago. This, of course, is not true; geographers have always insisted on measuring distances, elevations, populations, commodities, and so on. Actually the new reform movement urges that geographers strengthen the scientific content of their discipline through developing more theoretical concepts and testing them by refined mathematical-statistical procedures.

The modern quantitative method endeavors to measure exactly the extent of areal association between phenomena. This is called "correlation analysis." Take, for instance, the two variables of per capita gross national product (or income) and per capita consumption of mechanical power. Both variables have high values in the countries of Anglo-America and northwestern Europe, and both become progressively lower until we finally reach, say, New Guinea. In this case there is a high positive correlation in the geographic distribution of the two values; in other words, they covary positively to a high degree. Now let us add as third variable the percentage of the labor force engaged in agriculture. We find that this value is very low in countries of Anglo-America and northwestern Europe and becomes progressively higher among countries of Africa and Asia. There is, then, a negative or inverse correlation between the first two variables and the third.

High correlation between two variables is no proof of causal relationship. It should alert the observer to the possibility of cause and effect, but it is also possible that both variables are unrelated results of a third, unknown, factor. Or the correlation may be coincidental and of little significance, as in the instance where a geographer observed a close areal correspondence between the American manufacturing belt and the area where Ben Davis apples are grown.

A technique now widely used to portray the relationship between two characteristics in different places is the scatter diagram (Fig. 10). The position of each place on the diagram is fixed by plotting one variable on the vertical scale and the other on the horizontal scale. If the dots align themselves neatly in a line slanting upward from left

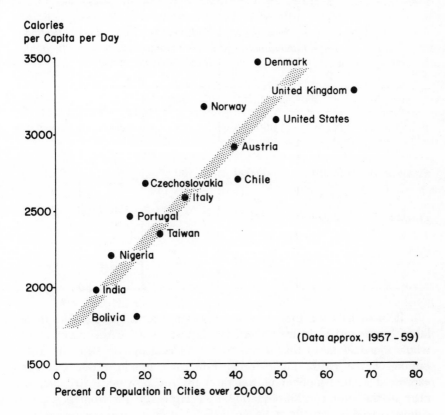

Fig. 10. Example of a Scatter Diagram. Although admittedly somewhat selective in the choice of countries, the diagram serves to illustrate the high positive correlation between proportion of population in cities and food intake, the latter as an indicator of level of living. Courtesy of Russell B. Adams, Department of Geography, University of Minnesota.

to right it indicates a high positive correlation. If the line slants down-
ward from left to right it indicates a negative or inverse correlation.
To measure much more precisely the degree of correlation requires
construction of a regression line. For fear of scattering our readers we
will not pursue this line any further.

Another, rather simple technique serves to measure the so-called
location quotient, that is, the degree to which a specific sub-area has
more or less than its share of a particular activity or quality present
in the total area. To illustrate we will determine the location quotient
of manufacturing industries for the four provinces of a hypothetical
country. The values given in the following table indicate that 20 per
cent of the labor force of Country X is employed in manufacturing.

	(1) *Number in labor force*	(2) *Number in manufacturing*	(3) *Column (2) as percentage of column (1)*	(4) *Ratio of province over ratio of country*	(5) *Location quotient*
Country X	10,000,000	2,000,000	20	—	—
Province A	4,000,000	1,000,000	25	$\frac{25}{20}$	1.25
Province B	2,000,000	600,000	30	$\frac{30}{20}$	1.50
Province C	3,000,000	270,000	9	$\frac{9}{20}$	0.45
Province D	1,000,000	130,000	13	$\frac{13}{20}$	0.65

If in each of the four provinces the same ratio (proportion) of the
labor force worked in manufacturing industries as in the country as a
whole it would mean that this activity covaried exactly with the distribution of the entire labor force. For each province this could be
expressed as the quotient of the ratio for the province (20) over the
ratio of the country (20), equaling 1.00. However, far from being that
simple, there is actually a heavy concentration of manufacturing in a
few provinces. Although Province A has the highest number of workers
in manufacturing, its proportionate share is less than in Province B,
which has actually the highest location quotient. Provinces C and D

have lesser shares in manufacturing when compared to the country as a whole, but D, with the lowest number of workers, has a higher quotient than C.

In the same way one could compute for each sub-area the location quotient of a particular industry, or the relative concentration of persons of a certain religion or language group or voters for a party.

Other techniques, some of them quite sophisticated, serve to determine such statistical measures as the coefficient of geographic association (or linkage), index of regional concentration, and coefficient of correlations. The reader interested in these advanced research methods may refer to the growing literature on this subject.[3]

The new techniques serve to test hypotheses which, if verified, result in theories that account in a logical and consistent way for the distribution or interrelation of phenomena. But theories are means to understanding the variety of the earth. They are not the ultimate purpose of geography. One must question, therefore, the excessive claims of those theoreticians who maintain that descriptive knowledge of particular places is merely grist for their mill, to be discarded as soon as the mechanistic theories of human behavior have been extracted.

The present wave of theoretical geography reminds one of the eighteenth-century belief in "rational man." The thinkers of those days reduced all man's actions to a few grand generalizations, true for all places and all times, as universal as Isaac Newton's law of gravity. They searched for symmetry of design. What did not fit into the general design was considered incidental, the result of human idiosyncrasies and not worth knowing.

What is the value of the new quantitative methods for the schools? And what about the new theoretical approach? As to the former, some of the statistical devices are within the grasp of the average high school student and could be effectively used to make him aware of modern techniques in the social sciences. As to theory, the well-trained teacher is accustomed to introducing pupils to general principles in verbal form. He could explain equally well such models as von Thünen's circles or the theoretical spacing of service centers. However, many of the current theoretical discussions are stated in complex mathematical formulas. If this means that little of the "new wave" will trickle down into the schools it is probably just as well. It would be hazardous to introduce radically new viewpoints which even in professional circles are as yet considered experimental and controversial (see also p. 78).

---

[3] I gladly acknowledge the use I have made for this section of the concise introduction to statistical methods contained in J. W. Alexander, *Economic Geography* (Englewood Cliffs, N.J.: Prentice-Hall, Inc., 1963), chap. xxxi. His bibliography is a good guide for further reading on this subject.

THE USE OF MAPS

The geographer has no monopoly on cartography, nor is he necessarily skilled in the cartographic techniques used, for instance, in geodesy, surveying, and photogrammetry. Nevertheless, there is a wide range of map-making concepts, techniques, and devices which are intimately associated with geography. Some geographers develop this field as a special branch, geographic cartography. For most of their colleagues, however, the map serves as a tool, certainly the paramount tool of the profession. Every geographer must have a working knowledge of cartographic presentation, not only to read maps but also to make them.[4]

Maps have two functions in research. First of all, they serve as the base to register geographic data, whether collected in the field or in the library. Secondly, the inspection of distributional patterns on two or more maps may uncover possible relationships. Every school child can and should learn the rudiments of cartographic recording and comparing. When L. D. Stamp started his land utilization survey of Great Britain he called on the school teachers to help him; 250,000 students did the actual mapping of the country, from which a series of highly informative maps were prepared. The third function of maps is to communicate the results of research in a more generalized form. In this category belong all maps for teaching purposes, regardless of level of instruction.

As to content, we may divide maps into two broad classes. One shows location of things or people, or of some of their inherent characteristics. The other presents relationships, often in the form of ratios. Examples of the first category are location of land forms, distribution of rainfall, population, crops, and minerals, but also distribution of religions and languages as special properties of peoples. Instances of the second are density of population, percentage of farmland in crops, number of births and deaths per thousand population.

Each kind of map presentation demands special techniques to convey a true and at the same time clear picture to the audience. Few people realize the thought and craftsmanship that go into designing a good map. By its nature the map is a positive statement. In writing about a topic one can tell the reader of one's doubts and convictions

---

[4] Those who wish to know more about maps and map making may want to consult A. H. Robinson, *Elements of Cartography* (2d ed.; New York: John Wiley & Sons, Inc., 1960); or F. J. Monkhouse and H. R. Wilkinson, *Maps and Diagrams* (2d ed.; London: University Paperbacks, Methuen, 1963).

and present conclusions with the necessary "buts" and "ifs." The cartographer has much less leeway. Even if he has cautioned by words or symbols that some of his data are less reliable than others, the map user is rarely proficient enough to appreciate these warning signs, and considers the map as a precise portrayal of reality. Like a poster, the immediacy of the picture can serve evil as well as good purposes. In Nazi Germany and in Fascist Italy, for example, maps were used intensively as propaganda for nationalistic aims.

Projections

A map is always an abstraction from reality. It starts as soon as we present the round earth on flat paper. Except for maps of very small areas the projection of the earth's curvature on a flat base inevitably causes distortions. If we want to retain correct shape we must sacrifice the right size of areas and vice versa. If distances are to be shown in correct proportion to reality, shape and size will be distorted. The choice of a specific projection depends, therefore, on the purpose the map will serve.

The Mercator projection, for instance, is admirably suited to the needs of the navigator because it shows true direction; its gross distortions of size and distance toward the higher latitudes make it unfit for educational purposes. In the same way, if one wants to show distribution of an item, such as population or crops, it is important that any square inch on the map represent the same number of square miles on the earth surface as any other square inch on the map. To gain this quality of equal area one must put up with distortion of shape. Equal area projections are widely used in American school atlases. To gain space for the display of land areas and their features the oceans are frequently omitted or only partly shown. These "interrupted" projections can easily lead to misconceptions of the relationships between land masses, unless the student has been sufficiently exposed to other, more complete, views of the earth. Most laymen are so accustomed to one image of the earth that all others look queer or even wrong. This is all the more reason to keep an open mind on map projections so that one gets used to viewing the world in different ways. Of course, one may always turn to the globe to see how things really are; unfortunately, our vision does not permit us to see more than one-half of it at a glance.

Scales

A map is a reduced representation of the earth's surface. The larger the scale, the closer the map is to reality and the more details that can be shown. Reduction in scale does not mean that items are merely shown in smaller size; much more important, reduction means selection of items to be shown, appropriate to the scale and the purpose of the map. Thus maps of different scales serve different types of analysis.

Topographic maps are representations on a large scale. If 1 inch on the map represents 1 mile on the earth's surface the numerical scale is 1:63,360. Many topographic maps use larger scales, such as 1:25,000. Maps on which 1 inch represents more than 1 mile are usually considered small scale maps. For a double page map of the world in a school atlas the scale is perhaps only 1:75,000,000 (about 1 inch to 1,200 miles), for a similar size map of the United States about 1:12,000,000 (1 inch to 190 miles).

Symbols

The cartographer uses a kind of shorthand which must be clearly understood to read his message accurately. For instance, most small scale maps of surface configuration portray elevation above sea level by layer tints for zones of altitude; say, shades of green for lands below 1,000 feet, yellow for the next higher zone, and so on. Some innocents interpret the green as indicating fertility, but even those who do not fall into this trap often think that the green indicates a flat plain and the darker shades mountains. In other words, they confuse elevation with local relief, forgetting that a surface below 1,000 feet may be quite hilly and a surface at 10,000 feet may be a flat tableland. The modern atlas makers are well aware of these misconceptions and use various devices to give a more plastic and naturalistic effect. For example, they combine the altitude tints with shaded relief or replace the conventional tints by a color scheme which resembles the hues of the local landscape as seen from an airplane.

Others do not use altitude layers at all but present perspective terrain drawings. This method not only requires great artistic skill but also intimate acquaintance with the physiographic forms to be depicted. Such drawings lose much of their value when reproduced on maps of very small scale. Moreover, the elaborately drawn terrain features do not tolerate many additional symbols (cities, roads) and lettering, lest the map become cluttered. Three-dimensional relief models are, of course, excellent devices for helping one understand terrain. They should accompany instruction from flat maps whenever feasible. The modern method of making relief models uses standard topographic maps printed on plastic sheets which are then molded by heat and suction around a master mold. One has to keep in mind, of course, that the vertical scale is purposely exaggerated in order to bring out even minor differences in relief.

Special Purpose Maps

In addition to the conventional "physical-political" maps there are a multitude of others which concentrate on special topics or themes, whence they are also called "topical" or "thematic" maps. The old-fashioned atlas contained few if any of them, but in its modern counterpart they far outnumber the conventional general maps. This reflects the change in emphasis from land forms, political boundaries, and place names to analysis of economic and social patterns. We will review them briefly in separate groups.

Discrete Symbols. The dot map is the best known of this kind, but the group also includes the use of other geometric forms (Fig. 2). Usually each symbol stands for a certain number of units in reality, such as one dot for 10,000 acres of cotton harvested, 5,000 head of cattle, or whatever the subject may be. A well-constructed dot map shows pattern and cluster as well as scatter of the item and thus gives a general impression of intensity of occurrence. The larger the scale the better the relationships to other features can be shown. On small scale maps, to avoid crowding, it is often advantageous to have each dot represent a fraction of the total, for instance, one dot indicating 1 per cent of the population.

Choropleths. Apart from the technical term, everyone knows this type of map, commonly used to show population density. As has been pointed out already (p. 36) the arbitrary size and shape of districts and countries as statistical units greatly affects the density pattern. Apart from this difficulty, the portrayal is influenced by the selection of the intervals for the density classes. Any teacher who is acquainted with the various methods of assigning grades from A to F to a continuum of exam points is aware of this problem.

In addition to all kinds of density patterns, choropleth maps can be constructed for other ratios, among them birth and death rates, calorie intake per capita, percentage of land surface in farms, percentage of population that is illiterate, or any other relation between two sets of information for which the census provides data (Figs. 3, 4, and 5).

Isometric Lines. There is no generally accepted terminology for this category, which includes all lines of equal value or ratio. Some use the term isarithm for any such lines, others refer to maps showing such lines as isograms. In this review "isarithm" is used for a line passing through points of equal value, and "isopleth" for a line passing through areas in which equal value exists.

a) Well-known examples of isarithms are the "isohyps" and the "isotherm"; the former, also called contour line, connects points of equal height above sea level, the latter points of equal temperature. Similarly, the "isobar" joins points of equal atmospheric pressure, the "isohyet" those of equal precipitation (Fig. 11), while the "isobath" passes through points on the sea bed which have equal depth below sea level. In all these cases there is a continuum of distribution. The distance between the isarithms indicates the degree of change on the earth's surface. For example, contour lines on a gently rising plain are far apart but get close as the slope increases.

b) In contrast to isarithms, "isopleths" are derived from points which express average values for statistical areas. For instance, instead of showing population density patterns by shaded areas, one can draw

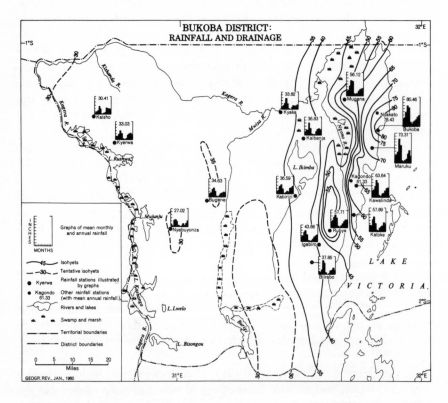

Fig. 11. Rainfall in Northwest Tanganyika (Tanzania), East Africa. An example of refined techniques of presentation, showing isohyets (lines connecting points of equal precipitation) distinguished by degree of accuracy, and graphs (histograms) of monthly rainfall at weather stations. From: D. N. McMaster, "Change of Regional Balance in . . . Tanganyika," *Geographical Review*, 50 (1960), 79. Map by D. N. McMaster. Reproduced by courtesy of the *Geographical Review*.

lines through the areas that fall within the same density class (Fig. 12). The resulting lines look like the product of scientific precision and reliability. But are they? In contrast to air pressure or slope, the change in population density is not necessarily continuous. Often we know only the average density figure for each statistical unit. Moreover, statistical units differ greatly in size and shape. How does one determine within each unit the proper point through which the line shall pass? Evidently, the essential trouble with isopleths is that they present characteristics of arbitrary areas as if they were actual values of points.

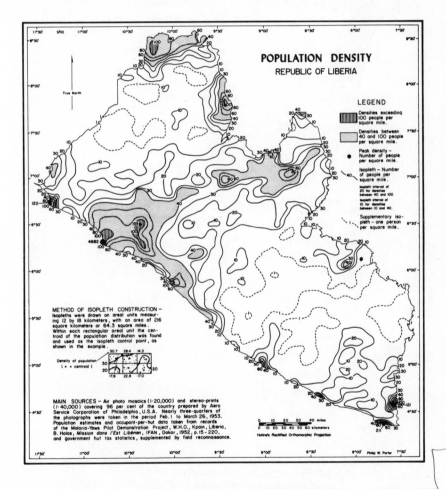

Fig. 12. Population Density in Liberia, West Africa. The density pattern is depicted by isopleths (see pp. 68–69). Shading is used where the bunching of isopleths would result in illegibility. Map by Professor Philip W. Porter, Department of Geography, University of Minnesota, and reproduced with his permission.

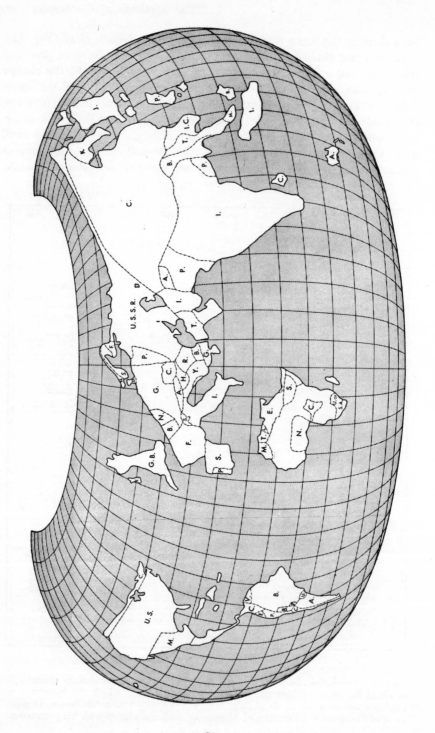

While this is not a serious defect in highly generalized small scale maps, it prevents the isopleth from being an exact research tool.

Miscellaneous Types. There are a number of other cartographic methods that do not fit into any of the previous groups. We have already mentioned the perspective land-form drawings, to which we may add block diagrams, cross sections, and profiles, each in its own way an effective means of depicting characteristics of place. Another type is flow maps, showing volume and direction of movement over a short or long time span, usually as arrows or bands whose width is proportional to the volume. The device can be used for air currents, river discharges, and movement of traffic, commodities, or migrants.

Another group comprises graphs placed within each area unit, among them bars for import and export, or production over a number of years, and pie graphs of, say, potential and developed water power. More involved diagrams sometimes shown on maps are graphs depicting average precipitation and temperature throughout the months, and population pyramids (Fig. 11). The advantage of placing such graphs in their proper location is, however, often counterbalanced by the difficulties of effective inspection and comparison if there are many of them, not to speak of the problem of fitting the graphs into small countries.

More stimulating are the various maps, or really statistical cartograms, in which the size of each country is presented in proportion to one of its other properties, such as population number or manufacturing output. This device portrays in a striking manner how large mainland China looms in population compared to Japan or the United States, or how the latter is the world's giant in manufacturing goods (Fig. 13). These cartograms are good antidotes for the hypnotic effect of the conventional map which merely shows surface area of countries.

Fig. 13. **Continents and Selected Countries on the Scale of Their Population (around 1950).** This "distortion diagram" brings out the comparative sizes of countries as measured by their population numbers. The grid of meridians and parallels is spurious. Originally published in W. S. and E. S. Woytinsky, *World Population and Production*, Twentieth Century Fund, 1953, p. 42. Reproduced by courtesy of the Twentieth Century Fund.

The
Essence   chapter six
of Geography

Geography provides meaningful insights concerning the earth as the human habitat. It is a way of looking at the earth, not an inventory of its contents. This viewpoint rests on a number of fundamental, interlocking concepts.

BASIC CONCEPTS

Many of the ideas presented in the following summaries of concepts basic to geography the reader has already met in fuller discussions in previous chapters.

The Cultural Appraisal of the Earth

The physical environment is not a rigid mold to which all peoples at all times must conform. Instead each society in each era perceives and interprets its physical surroundings and its relations to other lands through the prism of its own way of life. Only within this perceptual framework can the physical environment influence man. The modern notion of a "natural resource" reflects this view: It is man who perceives the value of some earth property and thereby creates a new resource. Through such technical achievement parts of the earth gain new value. Since interpretation of the environment depends on human circumstance, the prerequisite for geographic insight is awareness of cultural differences. It is always and only in relation to culture that the parts of the earth receive specific meaning.

This explains why modern geography stresses so much the quality of human resources. Economic progress of a country depends a good deal on its level of education, technical competence, entrepreneurial ability, social cohesion, economic organization, and political stability. Cultural regions provide a better framework than "natural" regions. Actually, the sharp distinction between "Man" and "Nature," so important in environmentalist thought, has lost much of its meaning in modern geography. The two form an interacting entity.

The Regional Concept

The regional concept is a device to comprehend likenesses and differences on the earth's surface. A region has some kind of internal homogeneity which distinguishes it from surrounding areas. Its distinct character may be perceived in the uniformity of its landscape features or in its mode of life, or it may be inferred from the way all parts work together in a functional system. A region is an areal generalization. It is always defined in terms of specific criteria.

The recognition of the region as an intellectual concept has led to a better understanding of the supposed dualism between topical (systematic) and regional studies. Both use the topical approach because the defining criteria are topical and both use the regional concept to identify areas of homogeneity.

Areal Coherence

The phenomena existing together in an area are not merely a jumbled heap of things, accidentally thrown together like objects on a city dump. Rather, they exist together in association, open to rational organization and comprehension. Such at least is the assumption with which the geographer approaches the study of places. It is comparable to that of the anthropologist who contemplates the seeming hodgepodge of culture, and to the proposition of the historian who faces the multitude of human events. This internal consistency unites the particles into a whole, what the French call an *ensemble*, and the Germans a *Gestalt*.

The interrelations between the elements are not the result of a single process; if this were so, one could trace all characteristics of place to a single cause, such as climate, relief, or form of government. Quite to the contrary, the conditions of the habitat, the character of the people, the use of the land result from a great variety of processes. We can not hope to account for everything within the spatial ensemble. But we can and must, within the context of the inquiry, determine the distinctive patterns and discover the nature of their relationships.

Spatial Interaction

Division of labor means specialization, but also interdependence. So it is with places: territorial specialization demands connection with other areas for the exchange of goods and services. In other words, areal differentiation and integration require interaction. Such interaction implies organization of space into some functional order or system, such as the spatial hierarchy of service centers. In turn, spatial interaction depends on circulation, that is, on the movement of messages, persons, and goods.

The situation of a place, its position in the web of circulation, is therefore of great importance in determining its character. Central location means high degree of accessibility, marginal location signifies isolation. However, to be in the center of things or events is not always an advantage; that depends on the nature of the phenomenon (war, tornado!). Innovations may be more successful on the frontier than in the center because the former is less burdened by traditions or vested interests.

Localization

Although implied in the foregoing paragraphs, the concept of localization needs emphasis in its own right. "Localization" means concentration of an activity in a limited area. In turn, it may attract other activities. For instance, a port city may draw shipbuilding and chemical industries, a textile district machine factories, a shopping center repair shops and a medical center. These phenomena of "linkage" result in nucleation of employment and population with characteristics different from those of surrounding areas. In measuring localization one seeks for intensity of occurrence rather than for mere distribution.

The Significance of Scale

On reflection it becomes clear that these concepts are equally applicable to small and large areas. For instance, in a large scale study we may search for the Gestalt of an area no larger than, say, Youngstown, Ohio, and its immediate surroundings. Its internal structure shows spatial interaction between town and country and between manufacturing, shopping, and residential districts, each localized in some particular part of the area. In contrast to this microcosm we may turn to the macrocosm of the United States; on this small scale Youngstown is a mere dot, subordinate to the higher order of localization of the iron and steel industry and its relations to other parts of the country as expressions of national differentiation and integration.

The scale of investigation makes, however, a great difference in the generalizations that can be drawn from the observations. For instance, while one might prove from a large scale study of a small area that the location of industries is strongly conditioned by taxes, zoning, and terrain, these factors would carry little weight in generalizations about the localization of industry in the United States or in the world as a whole. Or, general statements about a certain type of climate, while valid in a world-wide frame of reference, have only limited relevance in one valley where elevation, local winds, and sunny and shady slopes are much more significant factors.

Many disputes about the validity of observed regularities could be eliminated if opponents took careful note of the scale on which the investigation was conducted. For the same reason it appears fruitless to argue the merits of either macroscopic or microscopic studies. The nature of the problem should determine the scale of the inquiry, and the latter should in turn guide the degree of magnitude of the generalization.

The Concept of Change

The old notion of "the abiding earth" has given way to that of a world in flux. All the same, we could not live a rational life if we did not assume some permanence and persistence in nature and society. In a similar way the geographer describing what a place is like "at present" necessarily assumes a measure of endurance in the facts he has observed. At the same time he recognizes that the character of the area as he describes it is a product of the past as well as an interim phase in an ever changing existence.

Accepting change as a general principle, the rate and direction of change become the cardinal issues. Events must be viewed in time scales appropriate to the nature of their process. Atmospheric conditions are subject to daily and seasonal cycles; climate has fluctuated around a relatively constant mean over several thousands of years—it has changed over much longer time spans. Confusion of time scales leads to errors (much like confusion of area scales), such as interpreting the succession of a few cold years as the advent of a new ice age. The "cataclysm theory," current in the early nineteenth century, suggested (by analogy with volcanic eruptions and earthquakes) that the world's mountains and sea basins were formed by sudden earth catastrophes.

In human affairs we can observe similar short and long term changes, although even the longest are brief compared to the geologic time scale. Some are part of daily, seasonal, and annual cycles or fluctuations (e.g., commuter traffic, crop rotation, manufacturing output), others are long term processes modifying the way of life and the landscape (e.g., invention and spread of agriculture, European migrations, current urbanization).

Viewed in historical perspective, each place has its succession of patterns, expressed in dominant as well as recessive characteristics. In addition, the alert observer may detect mutations or innovations in the way of life which point toward future modifications. It is especially rewarding to view regions as expanding and contracting entities, perhaps even migrating ones. Somewhere a certain type of economy or a culture trait starts (the cattle kingdom, the cotton belt, the covered bridge, the sauna), puts its mark on the landscape, then spreads from there as far as conditions are favorable to its expansion. But a new resource may be discovered, or a different economy invades and transforms the area. The old region shrinks or may even become so overgrown and smothered by the new forces that at last only some relict forms remind one of the old order.

In short, the geographer must always reckon with change and understand its degree of regularity, its rate, and its direction. His work is never done, since every so often there is need for reappraisal. Even what is called "equilibrium" has meaning only as a temporary phase in the process of transformation. Thus evolution and revolution, cycle and fluctuation, stagnation and progress, tradition and innovation, retrospect and prospect, are mere variations on the theme of change.

DICHOTOMIES IN GEOGRAPHY

On several occasions we have pointed out seeming contrasts which on further thought proved to be subordinate part and counterpart of a broader entity. For instance, the dichotomy of regional and topical studies resolves itself in the larger concept of the regional approach; site and situation are the two aspects of place, and space and time are intertwined relations of reality. In addition, nature receives meaning through culture; function and form supplement each other as do quantitative and qualitative data.

Properly understood, these dichotomies are not divisive splits in the system of geographic thought; rather, they reflect complementary aspects or approaches, enriching our insights into the character of the earth as the world of man.

MEANS AND END

In conclusion, we will recall some of the views and counterviews on the nature of geography in the hope that they will guide us toward a better understanding of the scope and spirit of geography.

Geography as Biophysical Science

In the latter part of the nineteenth century when geology, meteorology, and botany made great strides, geographers were forcibly attracted to these fields. Many felt that here lay true science where they could establish cause and effect and discover "laws of nature." They concentrated on land forms, climate, and natural vegetation. Some even went so far as to exclude man because he was not open to "scientific" investigation. Today very few geographers, even if they work only with climate or land forms, would take such a dogmatic position.

Geography as Nature-Man Relationships

Another misconception, still common among laymen, is that geography's purpose is to discover how the physical (or natural) environment determines or at least conditions human behavior. This notion came to the fore in the latter part of the last century when Darwinian ideas seemed to offer answers to the evolution and variation of human societies. Social scientists were quick to develop grandiose generalizations: for instance, how the equatorial climate retards cultural progress while the temperate climate stimulates it. Such thoughts were not new (they can be traced back to Greek antiquity), but now they became the core of human geography. This form of geography remained firmly entrenched in the United States until about 1920. Although almost all American geographers have disavowed it since then, environmentalism still persists in many school texts.

Geography as Human Ecology

This variation on environmental determinism defined geography as the study of man's adjustment to the habitat. This view recognized that man is not merely a creature of the physical world around him but a force in his own right. Each society, having its individual cultural inheritance and technological equipment, finds a way to accommodate itself to the forces of nature. This approach, though an improvement over environmental determinism, remained caught in the misconception that nature is a given entity to which man adapts or adjusts according to his wits. Moreover, human ecology, like environmental determinism, concentrated on the local relationships of a society and its habitat, virtually ignoring interaction between areas.

Geography as Landscape Study

Diametrically opposed to environmentalism is the view that nature is passive and that human society is the active agent. A society uses its habitat and thereby changes the "natural landscape" into a "cultural landscape." The kind and rate of change depends on the culture of the occupying group. The landscape school aimed at the explanatory description of the visible features of the earth's surface as the expression of man's activity. This special approach, like all others, carried faults along with its merits. By tradition geography had always paid attention to the types of economy and the social and political order in their areal differentiation. Were these now to be banned except insofar as they explained visible landscape features? This criticism led to revision: it was admitted that there was more to geography than the study of landscape.

Geography as the Study of Distributions

The first question a geographer always asks about anything is: "Where is it?" Plotting the location of things or people on a map reveals their patterns of distribution. There can be no doubt that this is a very efficient way to discover areal relationships between two or more variables. But does this mean, as some assert, that geography can be defined as the study of distributions—"the where of things?" Rocks, plants, houses, people, all are somewhere on the earth's surface. Is the geographer supposed to plot distributional patterns of any and all objects? Where are his guide lines, his limits, in such an enterprise?

There is another and more important objection. Location of an object is an attribute of the object itself and, therefore, is a legitimate part of the concern of those sciences that study the object. One can hardly imagine that a zoologist in describing the tiger will ignore its natural range. However, showing the distribution of the tiger on a map does not make the zoologist a geographer. It all comes down to this: plotting distributions is a very important procedure in geography but not the distinguishing hallmark of this discipline. As a procedure it is a means to an end, not the purpose of geography.

Geography as Theory of Earth Space

From time to time the cry arises for a more scientific geography. The rationalists of the eighteenth century and the environmentalists of the nineteenth century wanted to make geography into a law-seeking science. Currently, there is a neo-rationalist movement among geographers, spurred by the wish to be "scientists," aided by mass data and powerful computers, and attracted by the federal funds so generously provided for the exact sciences.

Geography always has combined description of particular places with formulation of concepts and principles. Further strengthening of the theoretical foundations, therefore, is a necessary and welcome continuation of the tradition. The present interest in mathematical-statistical analysis of distributional systems and spatial interaction increases as well as refines our concepts of interrelations. Danger arises, however, from excessive claims which would restrict the horizons of geography to an abstract science of spatial relations.

The search for general laws, necessarily at a high level of abstraction, goes against the grain of geography because it removes place and time from our discipline. Geography is not concerned with universalized economic or social man, living on a planet as bare as a billiard ball. To the contrary, geography probes into the complex reality of localized patterns accumulated from the pluralistic history of mankind on the diverse terrestrial scene. Distributions are not simply determined by arrangement in a functioning system, like the position of jewels in a watch. They also, and chiefly, result from nonrecurrent historical processes. Thus, while the theoretical model of the spacing of towns or zoning of agriculture clarifies our thoughts by the sheer logic of the design, we geographers immediately follow it up with the question: How does it help us to understand reality?

Since massive quantitative data on human behavior are mainly available for the advanced countries, and then only for at best a century, the theorists tend to construct their models from facts of the "here-and-now," virtually ignoring former times and other cultures. The procedure becomes invidious when one projects the model derived from one's own surroundings over the whole world as a universal truth and measures different situations in other countries as "deviations" from the "ideal" construct. Geographers have always prided themselves on their broad interest in all countries and peoples. The parochial view, a–historical and egocentric, has no place in geography.

Conclusion

The comparison of these viewpoints, while seemingly negative, actually clears the way for a better comprehension of the nature of geography. All of them deal with *means* of geographic understanding rather than with the *end* of geography. Each emphasizes one concern to the exclusion of the others. Yet together they provide a fairly complete list of approaches to geographic knowledge. The geographer must learn about the biophysical features of the earth; is deeply interested in the interrelations between society and habitat; needs to read the cultural landscape as the earth-engraved expression of man's activity; inspects and compares distributional patterns; and formulates concepts and principles. All these means, each part of the whole, together serve the purpose of geography: to understand the earth as the world of man, with particular reference to the differentiation and integration of places.

Suggested Methods for Teachers

chapter seven

by
Raymond H. Muessig
and
Vincent R. Rogers

INTRODUCTION

For purposes of clarity, the intellect has to isolate the object of its attention from the whole within which it stands. Even when we try to extend the span of our interest as far as possible, the whole is beyond our grasp; it exists only in our vision, or intuition. Yet, without a picture of the whole we cannot even comprehend the single. Behind and within every leaf we see is whole nature, and it is the same with every person. And behind every person is also his society, his nation, and its history, mankind, and finally the universe. . . .[1]

In many respects Americans live in an age of super-specialization. They are familiar with football players who do nothing but kick, garage mechanics who work exclusively on automatic transmissions, and architects who are concerned with just interior designs. Yet specialization is not a completely new phenomenon. Herodotus—called the "Father of History" by Cicero and credited by some geographers and anthropologists with siring their disciplines—wrote this interesting passage on Egyptian medical practice:

> The art of medicine in Egypt is thus exercised: one physician is confined to the study and management of one disease; there are of course a great number who practice this art; some attend to the disorders of the eyes, others to those of the head, some take care of the teeth. . .

Specialization, however, is not without its problems and shortcomings. There is a persistent danger of obscuring entire forests with a

---

[1] Robert Ulich (ed.), *Education and the Idea of Mankind* (New York: Harcourt, Brace & World, Inc., 1964), pp. 22–23.

single tree, seeing a mote but ignoring a beam. There are specialists, indeed, in geography, but it is an unusually sweeping and integrative field. Contrary to an idea held by many laymen and even some classroom teachers, geography is much, much more than a monosyllabic response to an oversimplified question of "Where?"

In the study of geography the classroom teacher has an exceptional opportunity to help children and youth deal with interrelationships, to fit parts into wholes, to embrace larger conceptual configurations. Many understandings from other social sciences can be illuminated through and fused to major geographical insights—assuming, of course, that the teacher extends the perimeters of his approach to geography. If he sees geography as little more than names of continents, countries, capitals, and crops, no conceptualization or generalization will occur. If he hopes to reach higher intellectual levels, he must view geography as more than terms such as *meridian, delta,* and *tropical rain forest* or map skills such as using cardinal directions, orienting a map, interpreting map legends, and computing distance by the use of scale.

We believe that the five salient geographical ideas we have chosen to illustrate will encourage teachers to enlarge their own vistas and those of their students. Aspects of geographical instruction such as the teaching of specific map skills and many others have not been handled in detail here because of the abundance of sources already available to classroom teachers. The reader is reminded that this chapter contains no proposal for a given kindergarten–through–high school program in geography. Most of the ideas and suggestions tendered here can be used in existing curricula as well as in many newer, experimental programs.

1. Man's Use of the Land Is Seldom the Result of Any Single Physical Factor. Rather, Such Utilization Is Determined by the Interplay of a Number of Phenomena, Both Physical and Cultural.

A "place" includes a piece of land as well as the human group that occupies it. Much of "sunny California" owes its recent settling and rapid growth to the amenities of its particular and unique physical setting. Initially its location was far from the mainstream of trade and commerce; yet, willy-nilly, people heard of a "land of milk and honey" far to the west, and off they trekked in unprecedented numbers.

One must be wary, however, of oversimplifying the relationship that may exist between the character of a place and its physical attributes. California, for example, was and is inhabited by many people who moved there for purely economic or other reasons without any particular concern for climate; its population could never have grown to its present size without the existence of a level of technology that made mass migration convenient and relatively inexpensive. The pattern of living that exists in a given place, then, is the product of a variety of physical, social, political, and economic factors; it is seldom the result of any *single* cause.

Primary grade children might explore this understanding by creating a series of dioramas or models of their physical environment. The teacher could tell them that they can design a scene about anything they wish—*except* that it must be completely *natural*; nothing man-made should be depicted in their model. Initially it would be wise for both teacher and pupils to examine each diorama as it is completed since many children may inadvertently include man-made elements in their scenes. Having weeded out any unnatural factors that may have crept in, the entire class (or groups of four or five) might attempt to suggest some possible *uses* for the places created in each diorama—ways in which man might decide to take advantage of the physical environment. For example, Billy's forest scene could become a source of lumber: trees would be cut down, a sawmill constructed, roads bulldozed in, etc. Or, it might be used as a wildlife preserve or as a boy scout camp. Mary's lake might become a vacation resort, a means of transporting goods, a source of water for a nearby community, and so forth. As the class discusses each scene, a chart listing its possible uses could be placed next to it. Singling out one diorama and one of its suggested hypothetical uses, the teacher could ask the class to list the *reasons* that a group of people might decide to use Billy's land in a given way, i.e., as a source of lumber, as a wildlife preserve, or as a location for a boy scout camp. He might write on the chalkboard, "Billy's forest could be used as a boy scout camp if . . . ," and the class could supply a set of necessary conditions. For example, it would be useful as a camp *if* it were close enough to a city or town where there were enough scouts to make use of it; *if* there were good roads between the town and the camp; *if* the boys in the area were interested in scouting; *if* there were money enough available to build the camp, feed the scouts, etc. A number of dioramas might be examined in this way. Eventually the class could attempt to list the kinds of factors that influence the ways in which man uses the land. As many ideas as possible should be recorded, and the class may summarize its study by attempting to group or categorize them in some logical manner.

A second approach that might help younger children grasp this understanding involves the selection of a hypothetical home site. Two or three children might pretend that they have just moved to a new community and they are faced with the problem of choosing suitable land on which to build a house. A "real estate agent" (the teacher) shows them five pictures of possible locations: a heavily wooded lot, a site on the shores of a lake, a hilltop location, an open, flat area, and a lot overlooking a swift flowing stream. The "agent" urges the children to choose the one they like best. The group makes a decision (for the sake of discussion let's assume they choose the lakefront lot) and "purchases" the land. The "agent" might then tell the children that, while the lakefront lot was really quite pretty, he had neglected to tell them that the lake was polluted because a factory dumped its refuse into it, that it was located thirty-eight miles from the nearest school, and that the home would have no fire protection because it was too far out of town! The other pictures might then be used as a stimulus for a classwide discussion in which a great variety of "things to think about before choosing a place to build a house" could be listed. Eventually the children should begin to understand the number and variety of factors that may determine the desirability and usefulness of a given physical location.

Older students might consider this understanding through a similar lesson in which they attempt to decide on the location of a particular kind of industrial plant. They might be divided into committees of from four to six, each committee working independently. Eventually each group would present to the class a detailed description of the site they chose for the plant and the reasons for their choice. For example, the teacher might ask them to explore locations for a new aluminum plant. Students might first read about aluminum and discover that aluminum ore can be extracted easily and cheaply from bauxite. Without further consideration they might decide to locate a plant in Arkansas, Georgia, or Alabama where bauxite is found. A second group might find that huge quantities of inexpensive electric power are needed for the manufacture of aluminum. They could locate, then, in Oregon or Washington or elsewhere where there is an adequate source of power. Other groups might concentrate on transportation facilities; a ready supply of labor; inexpensive land for the plant site; favorable tax conditions; communities with medical, educational, recreational, and cultural facilities, pleasant climate, etc. Or, a group might locate the plant in an area where many things made of aluminum are being produced. The class could discuss and weigh the decisions of each committee and attempt to agree on one, best site—after carefully evaluating the *many factors* that must be considered when industrial executives make decisions concerning the location of a new plant.

Still another way to explore relationships among the phenomena that give character to a place involves what could be called a "community survey exchange." We might assume, for example, that an intermediate grade or junior high school class is studying the geography of the United States. Through either personal contacts or through the exchange lists that are published in magazines like *The Instructor,* the teacher could arrange for an affiliation with a class located in a community in a different part of the United States. Each class might then conduct a purely *physical* survey of its own community. While the specific format will vary depending upon the age and maturity of the students, this is the kind of information each class will be seeking:

> What is our weather like? Can we find average minimum and maximum temperatures for each month; the amount of rainfall, snow, etc.? Are there unusual wind currents that affect our weather? Are we subject to severe storms such as hurricanes and tornadoes? Do we have a dry or humid climate? (Obviously, it would be most helpful if each class could organize and categorize its information, using appropriate charts, graphs, tables, and drawings to illustrate and clarify wherever possible.)
>
> What does our land look like? Is it hilly, flat, mountainous, or swampy? Does it have a variety of topographical conditions within a small area? (Again drawings, photographs, and student–constructed maps would help clarify verbal descriptions of the lay of the land.)
>
> What kinds of soil exist here? Do we have mineral resources? What kinds of plants grow? What kinds of animals thrive here?

The first phase of the project involves the exchange of such data between the two classes. Then students in a Waco, Texas, school, for example (without recourse to *any other* source of information), might attempt to hypothesize about life in Marshall, Minnesota. What sorts of houses exist? What do people do for fun? How might people earn their livings? Are there farms? What kind? The class in Marshall could carefully read and discuss their exchange group's statements, compliment them on their accurate guesses about life in Marshall, and (politely) list their mistakes. The Marshall students should be sure to explain *why* their Waco friends were wrong: *why* certain occupations or industries suggested do not exist in Marshall. At the conclusion of the exchange project both groups should be able to see that many factors not revealed in the original community surveys also influence the pattern of life in a given location.

Another approach that might prove fruitful for teachers of older students involves a series of individual or group assignments dealing with major American cities. Each student (or each group) is assigned a city. The students are asked to explore as thoroughly as time and resources permit the city's birth, growth, and development and to identify factors which contributed to the growth of the city. We might expect a wide variety of factors to be mentioned, depending upon the particular city chosen. Eventually the students would share their findings and might come up with a general list including such things as proximity to natural resources, ease of defense, nearness to connecting waterways, the sudden development of a demand for products produced in the area, the establishment of political stability in a previously unstable area, the construction of a canal or railway, etc. These growth factors could then be categorized by the class as a whole; and the interrelationship between physical, political, economic, and other elements as they relate to the growth and development of a place should become clear.

The fascinating unfolding story of our government's interest in the construction of a new canal to replace the increasingly inadequate Panama Canal offers high school students an unusual opportunity to study the many factors that may affect the character of a place. A senior high school teacher might begin such a study by reading the following news item to his class:

> The need for a new canal is growing desperate. In the 50 years since U. S. Army engineers carved the present seaway out of the Panamanian jungle, the canal has proved one of the wonders of the world. Today some 50% of Japan's exports to the West pass through the canal; such South American nations as Ecuador, Peru and Chile depend on it for between 75% and 90% of their total imports and exports. But ships have slowly outgrown the intricate network of three lock systems that carry them across the hump of the isthmus, and trade is expanding far beyond the canal's capacity to handle it. Over the last ten years, commercial traffic has climbed from 36 million tons annually to almost 65 million tons. Today, some ships lie to for 15 hours or more awaiting their turn. The biggest tankers and aircraft carriers cannot squeeze through at all. With the trend to bigger and bigger ships, the canal will be obsolete altogether by the year 2000.
>
> President Johnson mentioned four possible sites—all of them publicly discussed on earlier occasions—for a sea-level canal to connect the Atlantic and Pacific without need of locks. One is a 95-mile route in northwest Colombia, another a 168-mile route slicing through Costa Rica and Nicaragua; the remaining two are in Panama itself—one running 60 miles through the southern Darien wilderness and the other, the present 51-mile waterway, which would need considerable widening and deepening to eliminate the locks. Johnson gave no hint as to which route the U.S. preferred, saying only, "I have asked the Secretary of State to begin discussions immediately with all the governments concerned." [2]

Following an initial explanatory discussion during which the points made in the news story are clarified, the class might be divided into committees. Each group would be assigned one possible site for the new canal, i.e., Colombia, Nicaragua–Costa Rica, and Panama. The first task

---

[2] *Time*, December 25, 1964, p. 16. Courtesy *Time*; copyright Time, Inc., 1964.

of each committee would be to undertake as thorough an evaluation as possible of the physical advantages and disadvantages of each site and present them to the class. Some students may be inclined to make hasty decisions because one route would be shorter, or perhaps pass through relatively level country, or incorporate a large natural lake as part of the canal, etc. The teacher, however, might insist at this point that the committees investigate the nonphysical factors that could affect the selection of a new canal site. He might remind them, for example, of the recent riots in Panama related to the "sovereignty in perpetuity" clause of the 1903 treaty between the U.S. and Panama. If the U.S. is to build the canal, what sorts of rights and guarantees should we have? Which country is most likely to be sympathetic to such arrangements? Should the U.S. "go it alone" or attempt to include other countries in the planning and construction of a new canal? What effect would the economics of a two-billion-dollar project be likely to have on a country's attitude toward the canal? How important a factor is the internal political stability of a country across which we may plan to build a canal? Is adequate manpower available or would American workers have to be recruited in inefficiently large numbers, etc.?

While no firm decision is likely to be made, the class should begin to realize that a variety of factors *will* and *should* affect our government's ultimate choice of a site for an improved Atlantic-Pacific canal.

2. The Evolution of Mankind from Isolated, Self-Sufficient Communities to an Interdependent Whole Means Ever More Trade, Migration, Diffusion of Ideas and Practices, and Greater Importance of Relative Location or Situation.

Thousands of years ago, as primitive man sloughed through the mire of swamps, forded treacherous streams, hunted (and was hunted by) a great variety of terrifying creatures, he sought little indeed in the place he was to call home beyond the needs of simple survival. A place that offered food and could be easily defended, a place reasonably dry and sheltered from the cold and the wind—this was all he asked. He lived literally (and often briefly) by his wits, and he counted on no one outside his small, intimate tribal group for help of any kind. To primitive man "neighboring" groups were synonymous with trouble, and he neither helped them nor sought their help.

Most of today's inhabitants of the earth find themselves in a vastly different situation. Their lives are wedded to their fellow man's to an ever increasing degree—witness the abject helplessness of many modern city dwellers, for example, when a natural disaster cuts them off even temporarily from the necessities they have come to depend upon from the outside world.

Man's relationship to man, then, has become increasingly important; places no longer exist in isolation, and the *relative location* of a given area has become of crucial importance to its inhabitants.

There are an almost infinite number of ways to make children aware of the many relationships that exist between their communities and the world at large. Teachers might, for example, conduct a community survey in which the class attempts to list the things that are produced "in *our* community" without *any* help from afar. While the list may appear fairly large at the outset, a continued investigation will reveal that few items do not depend ultimately on someone or something outside one's immediate location.

Similarly, a class might list every possible means of transportation in and out of its home community and then imagine that for one week all transportation facilities have ceased to operate; the town is sealed off from the world. What would be the effects of such a "breakdown"? What supplies would the town have? What would it lack? How long might it survive without outside help?

In a more complex vein, older children might examine a map of the "limits" of the city in which they live or of a city close to them. They might first discuss the technical interpretation of the term, "city limits." The teacher could then ask them if this is where the city *really* ends. One might expect that junior and senior high school students would be well aware of the fact that a modern city includes a string of suburbs as well as what is often referred to as the "central city." At this point the teacher might suggest that the class divide into a number of groups in order to study the relationship that exists between the city and the surrounding areas that fall within its sphere of influence. For example, one group might investigate one or more major city newspapers. An examination of the classified advertisement section generally reveals a wide variety of ads placed by people both "in" and "out" of the city. The students could construct a large map of the city and its surrounding area and plot the distribution of sample ads that reveal something of the size of the area covered by such material. The newspaper's circulation office would have information readily available on the range of its circulation and this information, too, might be plotted on a map. Other groups could contact the business offices of major entertainment enterprises such as a legitimate theatre or symphony orchestra for information concerning the area their mailing lists reach and, presumably, the area the theatre or orchestra serves. A city's major department store might supply information concerning its advertising-by-mail campaign: How many ads do they send out in a mailing? Where do the ads go? How far away do their customers really live? The class may obtain as little or as much data of this kind as time permits. Eventually, however, they ought to be able to construct, at their own level of maturity, a map or series of maps that should help them understand certain aspects of the relationship that exists between a city and its surrounding areas.

The increasing importance in the modern world of a place's situation or relative location may be explored in a number of ways. Students from the intermediate grades through senior high school, for example, might undertake a series of case studies of carefully selected communities within their state. To begin this experience the teacher could display a large map of the state with four or five towns and cities circled. One might be a small, rural town with a population of about 1,000. Another could be larger, a "county seat" of perhaps 10,000 people. A small city of 50,000 and a large urban center with over a million people might conclude the list. The class might then investigate the types of services each town provides for its surrounding area. They would soon discover that the small town of about 1,000 offers certain limited facilities, such as a food store, a post office, and a garage. The larger towns give considerably more services and interact with an ever increasing area. Finally, the huge metropolitan city supplies an almost infinite number of services that are usually available only in cities of such size. (One of the most simple yet thorough sources of information listing such services is, incidentally, the "yellow pages" section of the telephone directory. One may find there everything from hobby shops to health clubs, from demolition experts to specialists in destroying the records of defunct businesses.) When the class has gathered its data and clearly differentiated between the degrees of service provided by the four communities, the teacher might suggest that the students offer explanations for the growth and importance of the large urban center as compared to the other communities selected for study. Why, for example, is Chicago (or Minneapolis or St. Louis, etc.) an important metropolitan city while "Jonesville" remains a village of 1,500? While a number of factors may be mentioned, the city's central location—its high degree of accessibility, its position in the "web of circulation"—is certain to be a significant factor in explaining its growth.

An interesting and worthwhile follow-up to activities such as this involves talks by specialists from large oil companies, supermarkets, and other businesses which are faced with the problem of choosing sites for new branches. How *does* an oil company find a suitable spot for a new service station? A visit to the classroom by one of these experts might introduce students to the use of traffic counts, particular types of maps prepared as home-office aids in making such decisions, graphs charting anticipated increases and decreases in population growth, maps of current and projected highway construction, and so forth.

Perhaps one of the most fascinating stories of our time concerns the construction of Brazil's new capital, Brasilia. The city is far more than an architect's "dream project"; it is an impressive example of the importance of relative location or situation in the selection of a site. Senior high school students might explore the story of Brasilia as both a practical illustration of the geographer at work and a case study of the relationship between site and situation. After the class has developed a basic background of information concerning Brazil, the teacher might suggest that the students attempt a "brainstorming" session aimed at determining *why* many Brazilians wanted to move their capital from Rio de Janeiro to a new location. Eventually the teacher might list some of the real reasons many Brazilians give concerning their desire for a new location for their capital. For example, the Brazilian has an exceedingly warm feeling for those mysterious backlands, and he is anxious to see the area settled; increasing nationalism has created a desire to move the center of political activity inward, away from the outside world; some Brazilians think the original location of the capital in Rio de Janeiro served Rio's interests well, but not necessarily the interests of other parts of the nation.[3] The teacher could then mention that it was at this point that a group of geographers was asked to survey the interior and recommend an area within which the new capital might be located. The teacher could suggest that his class attempt to play the role of geographers in this situation. To begin with, the teacher might write these official instructions from the government on the chalkboard:

1. The new capital should be located somewhere near the demographic center of the country.
2. The new capital must be located in an area that is accessible from all parts of the country.
3. The new capital should lie on the border between two or more states rather than wholly within any one state.[4]

The class might break up into four or five "geographic-consultant" teams and begin their investigations. Eventually each group could make its proposal, using appropriate maps and other data to support its decisions. The students could then compare their hypotheses with the area originally mapped out by the geographers who actually worked on the project. Finally, the class might be given this list of principles which was to determine the selection of a *specific site* for the new capital:

---

[3] Preston E. James and Speridiao Faissol, "The Problem of Brazil's Capital City," *Geographical Review*, 46, No. 3 (July 1956), 304.

[4] *Ibid.*, p. 311.

1. Gently sloping terrain—not too steep, not too flat.
2. A comfortable climate with no extremes of temperature or rainfall and no violent winds, and at an elevation high enough to offer freedom from malaria.
3. A water supply adequate for a city of half a million people, preferably available by gravity flow.
4. Nearby forested areas where agriculture can become established for the supply of vegetables and milk, and where wood can be procured for fuel.
5. A source of low-cost electric power located within 100 kilometers.
6. Locally available building materials, including lime for cement.
7. A subsoil suitable for building foundations and for the excavation of sewers and subways.
8. An attractive landscape and nearby recreation areas.[5]

Ultimately the class should begin to see the primary significance of *situational* requirements in locating Brazil's new capital and to understand the secondary importance of site factors.

Somewhat similar techniques might be employed in a number of other situations. Students might be asked, for example, to imagine that Washington, D.C., is *not* the capital of the United States. The class is faced with the problem of choosing a new location for our capital: Where should it be located? Why? Can the location of our present capital at Washington be criticized? In what ways?

The increasing importance of a place's relative location in our air-age world might be made apparent to students in junior and senior high school through an exercise in which a series of places is described *initially in terms of site* characteristics alone. (The class should be told, however, that the places described *are* quite important.) For example, the following types of items might be included in a series of descriptions which could be mimeographed for each student's use:

Place "A"
This is a chain of islands that covers in all an area of about 6,400 square miles. Some small shrubs and mosses grow there, but there are no trees. The climate is very cold and foggy. The population survives largely through fishing. . .

Place "B"
This is a rocky peninsula which is largely a limestone "mountain" rising 1,400 feet above the water. It covers an area of about two square miles. . .

Place "C"
This is an island of volcanic origin. It is about 65 miles long and 2 to 18 miles wide. It has an area of about 463 square miles. Its climate

---
[5] *Ibid.*, pp. 313–14.

is hot and humid and it is also subject to a large number of serious wind storms each year. . .

It should be apparent that for a number of reasons, i.e., climate, soil, storms, etc., the advantages of site are somewhat limited in these locations. The teacher might then reveal to the class the names of the places described. The first is the Aleutian Islands, the second Gibraltar, and the third Okinawa. At this point the teacher might suggest that the class (either together or in groups) attempt a thorough analysis of the reasons for the importance of such relatively poorly endowed places. Other, similar locations that might be studied include Gander, Newfoundland; the area in Panama in which the canal was built; Anchorage, Alaska, and so forth. In each case it should become clear that it is *relative location*—position in relation to the rest of the world—that is largely responsible for their eminence.

As a corollary to a study of this sort, teachers of children from the intermediate grades through senior high school might urge their classes to maintain a bulletin board featuring current newspaper stories about places that have suddenly become important to us and to others despite their size, climate, wealth, etc. Surely the Cuban missile crisis is an excellent example of the significance of relative location; i.e., it was Cuba's location ninety miles from the American mainland that made the installation of Soviet missiles an impossibly difficult pill for our government to swallow.

Another, more sophisticated method of demonstrating the importance of relative location is the use of a limited "model" of reality. For example, a high school teacher might outline a hypothetical place called "Newland" on the chalkboard. Newland is rectangularly shaped: its length is 200 miles, its width 25 miles. It is a physically homogeneous area, with equal amounts of rainfall, similar temperature range, and soil conditions that are ideal for the production of cotton. The same level of technology exists throughout Newland, and its people share the same values, beliefs, and attitudes. At one end of this rectangular land is a factory that manufactures cloth out of raw cotton. Its sole source of cotton is the hinterland farms of Newland. In order to earn dividends for its owners, the factory can afford to pay the farmers $5.00 per bale of cotton.

Running the length of Newland (and through its middle) is a railroad. It charges $1.00 to ship one bale of cotton fifty miles. It costs Newland's farmers $2.50 to raise a bale of cotton.

Having sketched Newland, its factory, and its railroad on the chalkboard and recorded the data given above, the teacher might suggest that the class formulate some hypotheses about the possible ways in which Newland's farmers would use their land. It should be clear, for example, that a farmer 200 miles from the factory would lose money if he raised and shipped cotton to the factory. He might have to turn to subsistence farming, even though his land is similar in every way to the farms located within fifty miles of the factory. Next the teacher might suggest that we change certain conditions and see what effect this might have on land use. What would happen if transportation costs were to go up $1.00 per bale per fifty miles? If the factory had to lower its price to $3.00 per bale? If a cheaper method of transportation were suddenly introduced? If the demand for cotton went down and the factory closed its doors?

3. *Each Culture Tends to View Its Physical Habitat Differently.* *A Society's Value System, Goals, Organization, and Level of Technology Determine Which Elements of the Land Are Prized and Utilized.*

Each physical environment presents man with many problems, opportunities, and challenges. It also imposes very broad limitations and restrictions upon human behavior, though it does not dictate what that behavior will be. An individual culture colors people's perceptions of their surroundings and shapes their valuations and functional interpretations of their milieu. The countless settings in which human beings have located do not demand built-in, constant forms of response. A definite way of life does not inhere in a patch of ground, but is molded and remolded as days tumble into centuries. Man has, acquires, and creates needs; tries to translate aspects of his environment into need satisfactions; and assigns worth to those things which produce consequences he considers to be desirable. A natural element becomes a cultural asset—a "resource"—when man finds a way to employ it to serve his wants. It is obvious that man must have certain things for his survival such as the air he breathes and that blankets his earth. But he uses that same air in culturally different ways when he builds fires, sails boats, flies kites, blows poison darts, runs windmills, welds metals, transmits sound waves, warms and cools homes and cars, inflates tires, powers various tools and equipment, pilots aircraft, opens parachutes, launches rockets, and guides missiles.

Students from the intermediate grades through the senior high school can be provided with many exercises involving *cultural* interpretations of physical environments. These may be of a real or imaginary nature. They could be varied easily with respect to their complexity and abstraction level. In one such activity the teacher might create a description, and perhaps a map, of a fictitious country and give each pupil a duplicated copy. Only the natural setting would be treated. The written information might be something like this:

Dnal is a country about the size of our state. It is a peninsula bounded by the Retaw Sea on the west, south, and east, and the Skaep Mountain Range on the north. No spot on the peninsula is more than fifty miles from the sea. The Retaw Sea, connected with the Tlas Ocean by the Strait of Tew, is quite large and very deep in most places. The Strait of Tew is from three to six miles wide and several hundred feet deep. Many kinds of fish live in the Retaw. There are six mountains in the Skaep Range, from 5,800 feet to 10,300 feet in height. The mountains are snow covered during the winter months. There are five chief rivers in Dnal that come down from the mountains and flow into the sea. Dnal also has a group of deep lakes in the north, a few waterfalls, and some swift moving streams. During the late fall and early spring there is usually rather steady precipitation throughout Dnal. For a month or so during the summer Dnal can be quite dry. Most of Dnal is sunny and warm a lot of the time. Parts of northern Dnal are hilly and even rocky. There is also a section of grassland in the north. The Yellav Valley in central Dnal is several miles wide and many miles long and has unusually rich, fertile soil. Southern Dnal has some fertile spots; a few low, forest-covered rolling hills; and many flat, sandy beaches along the shoreline. Some natural gas, coal, and petroleum deposits may be found in Dnal. A high grade of marble has been discovered in a few places. There is some zinc, lead, copper, chromite, and iron.

Working independently, every young person would translate the verbal and pictorial data in his own way. While class members would be dealing with an imaginary country, they might find dictionaries, encyclopedias, almanacs, atlases, globes, maps, etc., helpful for definitions, reality-type orientation, general information, and technical assistance. Each pupil would hand in an unsigned paper for general class use based upon his hunches derived from the limited information available to him. The paper would deal with such things as the people who live in Dnal and their nature, activities, customs, housing, diet, dress, interests, problems, wants, and satisfactions; the crops grown, products produced, and services rendered; the country's exports and imports; and so on.

A student or two might come to the teacher with the comment that insufficient information had been offered on which to base any kind of sound reaction. At this stage the teacher should simply agree, praise the student for his reservations, and ask him to do the best he can with the data in his possession. Later the student should be encouraged to air his view in class so this aspect of the situation can be discussed.

The teacher should read some of the unidentified papers to the class or project them on the opaque projector so they might be studied by the entire group. At first students would probably concentrate on minute details, minor errors, little inconsistencies, and isolated omissions evident in various papers. Next, perhaps they would share some of the difficulties they encountered in the assignment. Then students could begin to realize that even the things they had written which *were* faithful to the conditions outlined were divergent and contrasting. The class should finally arrive at the understanding that, while the physical milieu created for their study did have some givens, restrictions, and potentialities, it could be perceived and utilized in many, many ways by various societies and cultures.

Immediately following this approach, the teacher could shift the focus of the class from an imaginary to a real setting. After carefully selecting a single contemporary country or region of a country, the teacher could direct the class's attention to the current lifeways of its inhabitants. Next, the class would look at some of the many uses that man has made of the land at different times and/or under varied circumstances in history. Students might find that the physical environment itself has undergone certain changes over the centuries but that these changes in and of themselves furnish only a partial, less than satisfactory explanation of the broad cultural spectrum that has come within their view. They may uncover five or ten or more uses man has made of the water, the soil, the minerals, etc., through the years and under modified circumstances. The same general spot might have been used at different times as a grazing place for sheep, a vineyard adjoining a monastery, a work center for a craft guild, a school, and a university. On the same river one might have seen canoes, sailing ships, flatboats, log rafts, waterwheels, steamboats, tugboats, dams, hydroelectric plants, floating refuse from mills, and speedboats. Through this procedure students may come in contact with a number of economic, political, educational, technological, and other cultural factors that influenced man's views and uses of a given physical habitat.

The preceding activity could lead to still another step. This time the teacher might form four committees. Each committee would be assigned one specific physical environment. The four physical settings would be selected from different parts of the world. Committee A and Committee B would have contrasting physical habitats inhabited by societies with strong cultural similarities. (One might choose, for example, Lancaster, England, and interior New South Wales, Australia; San Diego, California, and Boston, Massachusetts; or possibly the Spaniards in Castile, Spain, and Costa Rica.) Committee C and Committee D would have very similar physical habitats occupied by people with substantially different cultures—perhaps Tucson, Arizona, and Fes, Morocco; or Minneapolis-St. Paul and Mukden, North China. Each committee would conduct its research initially without any knowledge of the comparisons built into this class activity. After adequate preparation a pupil would be chosen by his fellow committee members to present that group's findings to the total class. Following the four reports the teacher could start with a general class summary and evaluation of what was said and then guide his pupils to a deeper understanding of the ways in which a society's culture may affect its use of the land.

Another approach the teacher might employ to help children or youth gain some grasp of this third major idea has something of a Socratic or dialectic flavor. The teacher might begin by asking his class what a "natural resource" is. His pupils might have some difficulty defining "natural resource" and would perhaps recall from past study classes of natural resources (sunshine, air, water, soil, minerals, forests, wildlife) or specific examples, such as rivers, coal, pine trees, and salmon. Without comment the teacher could write on the chalkboard all the examples put forth by the class. Often students have no functional, transferable idea of why the things they have seen and heard listed as natural resources are given this label. They have learned to respond in a rote fashion. Next, therefore, the teacher would ask his class to think about the items that have been recorded as natural resources and to see what these items have in common. With a bit of fumbling a pupil or two may arrive at a rather loose statement like, "Natural resources are things that have always been on the earth."

Now the teacher is ready to help the members of the class refine and sharpen their thinking and to aid them in seeing the cultural relationship to natural resources. He could underline any one of the words on the board, for instance COAL, and then make an independent assignment. The class would have access to a number of materials in the classroom dealing with natural resources in general and coal in particular. Every pupil would be given a series of questions such as these and asked to answer them in their *numerical order:*

1. Is coal a natural resource?
2. Have we always had coal on the earth?
3. Have people always used coal whenever and wherever they found it?
4. Have people in different times and places always assigned the same value to coal?
5. If people had never used coal for any purpose would it still be one of the first things listed as a natural resource?
6. What do people mean when they say "carrying coals to Newcastle"? Why and when did people start using this expression?

Does this saying tell you anything about natural resources in general and coal in particular as a natural resource?

7. What are some of the things for which coal has been used? Have the uses made of coal always been the same through the years? Why?

8. Is coal more important, as important, or less important in the United States today than it has been in the past? Why? Does your answer tell you anything about natural resources?

9. If all of the coal in the world should be used up some day, what natural resources might be used to do some of the same things for which coal is now used?

10. What is a natural resource? Can you write your own definition now?

11. What have you learned about natural resources through this activity that you did not know before?

12. What questions do you now have about natural resources for which you would like to find answers?

As a result of their search for answers to questions such as the preceding, students might find that some coal existed as long ago as 400 million years and that coal is being formed today, although in very limited quantities. They might discover that man may have used coal 4,000 years ago, that it was burned for Bronze Age funeral pyres, that it is mentioned in the Old Testament, that coal was known to the ancient Chinese and Greeks, that the burning of this substance was punishable by death during the rule of England's King Edward I, that the Pueblo Indians utilized coal in the making of pottery, and that almost endless chemical products have been developed from this soft rock. They could see that the degree to which a natural resource like coal is tapped, expended, conserved, and prized can be related to factors such as the nature of and directions being taken by a given society, the spirit of the times, the abundance of the resource, and so on. They may learn that a natural resource valued highly in one culture is unknown, ignored, or assigned little worth in another culture; that a natural resource considered vital in the past may receive less attention in the present or even be ignored; that one natural resource may be substituted for another one for a variety of reasons; and that a natural substance which is yet undiscovered, unneeded, or unused today could be a prime resource tomorrow. They would almost surely develop a more meaningful understanding of what is meant by a natural resource and the importance of its cultural connotations.

An allied procedure would be to ask pupils whether *snow* is a natural resource. Initially the class might say that it is not—perhaps because it has not appeared on lists of natural resources they have seen, or because it comes and goes in their area, or because their parents have told them it is a nuisance. Then it might be observed that melted snow is water and that they have said that water is a natural resource; hence snow is also a natural resource. At this point the teacher could press the class for other illustrations of snow as a natural resource. If the class does not respond, the teacher might ask, "Is snow a natural resource when children play in it and people ski on it and Eskimos run sleds on it?" Soon it might be agreed that snow *is* a natural resource. Next, the teacher could ask the class whether they have heard about the man-made snow (atomized water and compressed air combined at 30° or below) being produced. He could show his charges a picture of powder snow being sprayed on a hillside.[6] He could point out that this may mean more ski resorts in places that usually do not get snow and that this snow is more reliable and lasts longer than "real" snow. The teacher might ask at this stage whether the sprayed snow is a natural resource. Some confusion might well ensue here. A perceptive pupil may comment that the water and air used in the machine are natural resources but that he is not so sure about the snow itself. Eventually someone may suggest that the man-made snow is an example of man's understanding of a portion of his environment and his capacity to "co-operate with nature." Through a variety of illustrations students may see that man can work within a natural framework to discover, use, preserve, modify, and extend natural resources to satisfy his needs. Students may mention such things as game preserves, fish hatcheries, efforts to rid streams of pollution, and so on. They could write for many booklets that would give them added insights into man's utilization, conservation, and improvement of his environment.[7] Examining just the recreational dimension, they could look at growing national interests in camping, hiking, boating, fishing, etc. On the international scene, they could return to the topic of snow that initiated their study and find that some countries that have in the past taken little advantage of the recreational possibilities of snow are beginning to do so. Japan, for instance, is experiencing a skiing craze.

Finally the teacher might use a method involving dyadic sociodrama to help his charges get closer to this third basic geographical generalization. Pairs of pupils in the class would be given problem situations to investigate thoroughly and eventually to role-play in front of the class. The teacher would identify some aspect of a particular physical habitat and briefly describe two hypothetical individuals who represent different

---

[6] See "Recreation: Where It Never Snowed Before," *Time*, January 1, 1965, p. 43.

[7] One example is *From Tree Farms to You*, a free booklet that deals with the story of tree farming and wood products and that has been advertised as available through Weyerhaeuser Company, Box A3, Tacoma, Washington, 98401.

periods of time, cultures, chronological ages, experiential bases, value systems, educational backgrounds, or levels of technical skill which might lead them to have divergent perceptions of this single aspect. With a little creative thought on the teacher's part, the socio-dramatic situations could be conceived at conceptual levels all the way from the primary grades through the senior high school. The information given to pairs of students could be quite detailed and proscriptive or very brief and open ended. A Plains Indian and a white hunter who shoots buffalo for sport could be brought together, just as an example. Or, a Pawnee Indian from yesterday and a Missouri farmer today could discuss the raising and use of corn; an orange grower in southern California might talk with a big contractor who is buying up groves, cutting down the trees, and building large housing developments; a trout fisherman who has signed a petition to keep power boats off his favorite lake might argue with a boating enthusiast who wants the lake opened for water skiing.

4. Every Region Is an Area Homogeneous in Terms of Specific Criteria Chosen to Delimit It From Other Regions. This Delimitation Is Always Based on an Intellectual Judgment.

A region is a creation of man—it cannot exist without his cognizance. It can best be understood, perhaps, if one views it as a *device* or *tool* of the geographer, a device that helps him to categorize and put in order the almost limitless variety of physical and cultural phenomena that exist upon the earth.

California's fertile central valley is a region, as is the semi-arid American southwest, Appalachia, the Great Plains, Florida's southern swampland, and an almost infinite number of other, similar divisions and subdivisions. *How* one decides to regionalize—where he decides to draw his boundaries and focus his attention—depends entirely upon the nature of the problem or question with which he is concerned.

Man's local, state, national, and international problems can acquire more meaning if grasped in a regional context. It seems to us that regionalization is a crucial understanding for countless reasons today. It is something that can be explored at every level in our schools with varying degrees of complexity and rigor. An understanding of this generalization could emerge through innumerable classroom techniques.

Senior high school students, for example, might eat their social studies cake and still have a piece of literary pastry by approaching regionalization through the lovely, patriotic, ethnocentric, provincial passage eloquently and sentimentally delivered by John of Gaunt, Duke of Lancaster, in Shakespeare's *King Richard the Second*:

> This royal throne of kings, this scepter'd isle,
> This earth of majesty, this seat of Mars,
> This other Eden, demi-paradise,
> This fortress built by Nature for herself
> Against infection and the hand of war,
> This happy breed of men, this little world,
> This precious stone set in the silver sea,
> Which serves it in the office of a wall
> Or as a moat defensive to a house,
> Against the envy of less happier lands . . .

Following the reading of this excerpt and a general discussion of its meaning, students could look at possible reasons behind its writing and the spirit of the times in which it was created. They might probe portions such as a "fortress built by Nature" and a "precious stone set in the silver sea." They could investigate whether the region called "England" was always "England" and even whether in fact its physical shape was always the same. (England and France were connected before the English Channel was formed.) Then, with an adequate background, the students could examine the controversy over the construction of a tunnel connecting France and England under the Channel. They could be asked why there is still such resistance to the idea when there is only a twenty-mile distance between Dover and Calais and when the channel can be crossed in seconds by supersonic planes and missiles. A number of ideas centered around regionalization would emerge naturally and could be transferred to other areas.

An unusually appealing example of a region as a mental picture which could be used with students from the upper elementary grades through the senior high school level is found in *Anna and the King of Siam*:

> The only map [the royal pupils] had ever seen was an old one that had been made twenty-five years or so before. . . It had been drawn by the prime minister of that time, who was a better politician than cartographer. It was five feet long and three wide. In the center was a ground of red, twenty by twelve inches. A human figure as long as the red patch was cut out of silver paper and pasted on it. This was the King of Siam. . . .

> . . . [Anna] sent a request to the King for maps and globes. His majesty responded promptly with a large English map and globes of the celestial and terrestrial spheres. These created an enormous sensation when they arrived one morning in the Temple of the Mothers of the Free. The King had caused the map to be mounted on ponderous gilt support-

ers in the middle of the temple. For nine days crowds of women came to be instructed in geography and astronomy. *It was hard for them to see Siam reduced to a mere speck on the great globe.* [*Emphasis added.*] The only thing that comforted them was that England, their teacher's country, was smaller yet.[8]

Class members might discuss the original and the altered image the royal pupils had of their country and possible concomitant understandings and attitudes with reference to "region" that might have developed. Or, the class might be shown one of those cartoon maps of Texas as perceived by a Texan, in which the Lone Star State covers most of the region usually known as the United States!

Children in the primary grades might be introduced to an aspect of regionalization through a role-playing activity built around this sketch:

Mr. Wilson works for a company that has offices in many different cities. He is such a good worker that his company has given him a better job in another city. He has a wife and four children. Robbie, age nine, is the oldest child. Melissa is eight years old. The twins, Teddy and Pam, are six years old. Mr. and Mrs. Wilson and the four children are staying in a motel and trying to find a home. The Wilsons have looked at ten homes, but they have not found one big enough for all of them that they can afford to buy.

In the newspaper Mr. and Mrs. Wilson read about a house that is for sale. It has four bedrooms and two bathrooms, a garage and a large back yard. The house does not cost too much either. It sounds like just the house the Wilsons want. The Wilsons decide to eat lunch in the motel restaurant and then go out to see the house. While they are eating, Mrs. Wilson says, "I wonder if something could be wrong with the house. It's big enough for us. It's one that we can pay for. Why doesn't it cost as much as the other houses we looked at?"

Following the reading of the story, the teacher asks the class to suggest factors that might explain the lower price of the house in the light of the things it offers. All the children's comments are then summarized by the class and written on the chalkboard by the teacher. At this point each class member is given a reproduced copy of a very simple map the teacher has drawn on a fluid duplicator master which depicts a three-block area around the imaginary house. The teacher reviews the little legend at the bottom of the map and answers any questions that arise about the map itself. Then the teacher asks the children whether the map suggests any reasons why the price of the

---

[8] Copyright © 1943, 1945 by Margaret Mortenson Landon. Reprinted from *Anna and the King of Siam*, pp. 104–105, by Margaret Mortenson Landon by permission of The John Day Company, Inc., publisher.

house is not as high as that of other homes that are the same size. The map might reveal a busy street in front of the house which the children would have to cross to go to school, a railroad track a block from the house, and a large oil refinery adjacent to the railroad track. After the students had pointed out drawbacks such as these, the teacher might ask whether the Wilsons will buy the house. All the children might be agreed that the Wilsons should continue their search for a home. But regardless of the class members' opinions, the teacher would then produce a second map. The map would be identical to the previous one at its center but would incorporate a six-block area surrounding the home. In this enlarged area the children would discover Mr. Wilson's office building, a church to which the Wilsons could go because of their religious faith, a large shopping center, and a huge neighborhood recreation facility that includes an outdoor swimming pool. The teacher would ask what the reaction of the Wilsons might be upon learning these things.

The primary teacher could use this same general approach in a gradually extended fashion until children understand that a region can be as small or as large as one wishes or is able to conceive it, maintain some form of homogeneity, and perceive certain interrelationships. The imaginary house can be taken in isolation as a region, as can the three- or six-block surrounding areas, and so on.

With pupils in the intermediate grades, the teacher might reverse the procedure and go from the general to the particular. For instance, a map of the North American region might be displayed and the children asked to trace the outline of the United States. This could be followed immediately with a map of the United States and the request that the class point out the region that man has designated for their state. Next, a map of their state would be used, and the boys and girls would identify their city region. And finally a city map could be studied until the region served by their particular school could be outlined. Following this visual initiatory activity, the class could be formed into five regional committees: one for North America, one for the United States, one for the state, one for the city, and one for the school neighborhood. Each small group could study its region in some depth, looking into such things as reasons behind the designation of the region as such, the history of the area, the over-all personality of the region, and some specific components found and tied together in the area. Each regional committee would make a presentation to the class, with every child having the chance to report on one aspect of the region. Then each of the five committees would elect a representative to join a central group which would be given additional time to gather information, formulate some ideas, and prepare for an additional report. In this class meeting vital relationships between and among the five regions would be treated. During the presentation itself and the class discussion after it, the children could discover that the labeling of a region has an arbitrary dimension to it; that regions have been known by different names assigned by men to them in the past; that generalizations differ for regions of different size; that none of the regions studied is completely autonomous; and that boundary lines exist only in the minds of men. (At the same time that this method just suggested is being used, incidentally, the teacher could do a number of things with map scale. Several understandings and skills relevant to scale could be introduced or reinforced through the use of a group of maps of the same outside measurement but dealing with different-sized regions and areas within those regions.)

Another, simple way to introduce the process of regionalization to children at a variety of grade levels involves the use of a state vacation or travel guide. The class might begin by examining the booklets published by a neighboring state or two. They should quickly notice that the typical vacation guide divides the state into a number of areas or regions in terms of their differing appeal to visitors. New York's guide, for example, might emphasize the ocean beaches of Long Island, the Adirondack mountains, the Finger Lakes region, etc. The teacher could then suggest that the class might create a similar booklet for *their* state, attempting to divide the state into a number of regions in terms of the areas' vacation attractions. Having regionalized on the basis of this set of criteria, the class might make similar booklets or pamphlets designed to attract industry to their state. In this case, of course, the subdivision of the state would be carried out on the basis of an entirely different set of criteria. In both cases, however, it should be clear that the "region" is both a useful tool and a construct of the mind.

Many elementary *and* secondary school students have been misled by the overabundance of political maps used both in and out of school. The tendency to distinguish one country from another by *color* gives an impression of uniformity that simply does not always exist. Any country, no matter how small, may be areally reorganized on the basis of a variety of criteria. Perhaps some of the emerging African nations offer particularly fruitful opportunities for study of the relationship between a country's political problems and its regional divisions. The Congo's difficulties, for example, can be far more easily understood by examining the Congo in terms of resources rather than of political divisions. The mineral wealth of Katanga obviously sets it off from the rest of the Congo, and the desire of some Katangese for political independence can certainly be understood if not necessarily condoned.

From the intermediate grades on through the senior high school, aspects of regionalization could be given countless historical, philosophical, psychological, political, economic, social, cultural, and physical underpinnings. For example, an intermediate teacher might write on the chalkboard some names commonly assigned to various states such as the following:

The Peninsula State	The Golden State
The Cornhusker State	The Panhandle State
The Silver State	The Gopher State
The Treasure State	The Bluegrass State
The Prairie State	The Bay State
The Beehive State	The Garden State
The Green Mountain State	The Cotton State
The Old Dominion State	The Evergreen State
The Cactus State	The Keystone State
The Sunflower State	

The children in the class might be asked to find out the precise meaning of the names, their origins, their accuracy in characterizing facets of particular regions, and so forth. In the process of investigating the names of states, the class would have a number of interesting contacts with dimensions of regionalism. In addition to being called "The Old Dominion State," for example, Virginia is also known as "The Mother of Presidents" and "The Mother of States." The last title stems from the fact that the original Virginia territory eventually became several states. The children could see in this instance a definite change in the mental image of a given region. The secession of Virginia from the Union also triggered a regional alteration when its settlers in western counties remained loyal to the Union and West Virginia was born. West Virginia itself has had an intriguing label applied to it which might launch a fruitful discussion. It has been called "the most northern of Southern States, the most southern of the Northern States, the most eastern of the Western States, and the most western of the Eastern States!"

We would expect the class to eventually conclude, however, that a *state* is a rather arbitrary political entity rather than an area that is readily distinguishable from its neighbors because of its unique physical and cultural features. This could lead to an examination of the ways in which the United States has been "regionalized" in various geography and social studies textbooks. A list including such labels as Corn Belt, Appalachia, Manufacturing Belt, The Great Plains, and many others might be put together. The class could attempt to evaluate the rationale behind each regional system, looking also for obvious overlap, inconsistencies, etc. Finally, having examined "regions of the United States" as perceived and organized by twentieth-century man, the class might be shown a map depicting Indian ways of life in their regional settings (Fig. 14). It should eventually become clear that a region is a cultural construct that varies in terms of the group perceiving it.

Junior high school students might investigate items related to regionalization such as the sectional compromise on the location of the permanent seat of our national government, the Louisiana Purchase, the Missouri Compromise, The Dred Scott Decision, the War Between

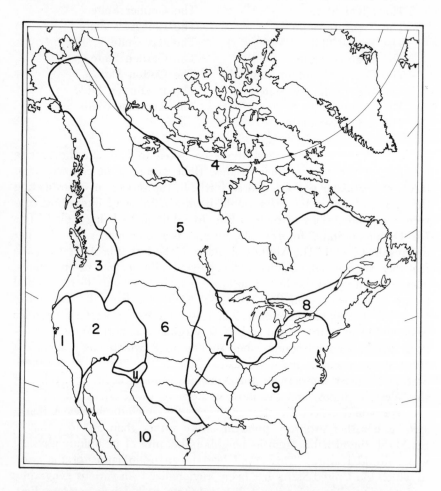

Fig. 14. Ways of Life of the American Indians about A.D. 1600. 1. Gatherers of California, 2. Gatherers of Deserts and Mountains, 3. Fishing Peoples of the Northwest, 4. Arctic Hunters, 5. Hunters of the Subarctic Forests, 6. Hunters of the Great Plains, 7. Hunters and Farmers of the Prairies, 8. Hunters and Farmers of the Pine and Maple Woods, 9. Farmers and Hunters of the Eastern Woodlands, 10. Hunters and Gatherers of the Southern Deserts, 11. Pueblo Farmers. After C. O. Sauer, *Man in Nature* (1939), by permission of Charles Scribner's Sons.

the States, the purchase of the Alaska territory, the homestead laws of the 1800's and early 1900's, and so on. The Alaska purchase, for instance, reveals some interesting attitudes held about that region by a number of Americans who referred to it as "Seward's Folly" and "590,000 square miles of icebergs and polar bears." Alaska could be discussed in many veins, each with a regional orientation.

Finally, pupils at various instructional levels might be asked to explain an event that occurs every summer in a little Midwestern town. While the town is less than a square mile in size, it sponsors a free annual picnic that is attended by people who live as far away as ten miles. At first it might seem odd to students that a relatively small group of people in a very limited area would purchase, prepare, and serve huge quantities of food to "outsiders" who are nonresidents of their immediate community. After various ideas have been exchanged by members of the class, the teacher could explain that the big barbecue is a means employed by local merchants, barbers, service station operators, doctors, and others to express their gratitude to the many farmers in the surrounding territory who spend their hard-earned dollars in town. The little town itself could not provide an adequate living for businessmen. The townspeople depend upon the extended community and tend to see it as their region or as a wheel integrally connected to the much smaller hub of the town. Students might be invited to discuss as well why a large number of people in the region surrounding the town know each other intimately while people in another region as small as a metropolitan city block or even a single apartment house might never meet to become acquainted. They might arrive at the discovery that a partial explanation for this situation lies in individual outlooks regarding different regions.

5. *The Character of a Place Is the Product of the Past as Well as an Interim Phase in an Ever Changing Existence.*

The hour was early; the morning still, warm, and beautiful. Shimmering leaves, reflecting sunlight from a cloudless sky, made a pleasant contrast with shadows in my garden as I gazed absently through wide-flung doors opening to the south.

Clad in drawers and undershirt, I was sprawled on the living room floor exhausted because I had just spent a sleepless night on duty as an air warden in my hospital.

Suddenly, a strong flash of light startled me—and then another. So well does one recall little things that I remember vividly how a stone lantern in the garden became brilliantly lit and I debated whether this light was caused by a magnesium flare or sparks from a passing trolley.

. . .

Hiroshima was no longer a city, but a burnt-over prairie. To the east and to the west everything was flattened. The distant mountains seemed nearer than I could ever remember. The hills of Ushita and the woods of Nigitsu loomed out of the haze and smoke like the nose and eyes on a face. How small Hiroshima was with its houses gone.[9]

So wrote Dr. Michihiko Hachiya in *Hiroshima Diary*. The passage illustrates in the most tragic of terms one of man's contributions to the ever changing pattern of life upon this planet. Fortunately not all of his efforts produce such dire consequences. A full accounting of the ways in which man has altered his physical environment would have to include his successful attempts to control floods, to restore exhausted farm land, to change the shape of the land so that a railroad or canal may be built, thus bringing a measure of economic prosperity to a formerly isolated area, and so forth.

Nature, too, contributes her share to the process of physical change. Sometimes slowly and sometimes with devastating speed she inundates the land, shapes and reshapes the hardest rock, creates a mountain and destroys a forest. Knowledge of the legacy of the past as well as an awareness of the ever present process of change are essentials of the geographic mind, and should be an important aspect of any school program in geography.

Kindergarten and other children in the primary grades may be introduced to the concept of change in a variety of ways. Virginia Lee Burton's Caldecott-award-winning book, *The Little House*,[10] for example, might be read to a group of first graders. The story concerns a house built on a hill, far out in the country. One day a road is built; soon new houses are constructed, and little by little the city creeps closer to the little house. At last the house is shown surrounded by skyscrapers, apartment houses, buses, trucks, and an elevated railway. Following the reading of the story the teacher might discuss the things that happened to the little house and why they occurred. Eventually the children could be asked to look for evidence of change in their own areas, such as the construction of a new house, the building of a bridge or tunnel, etc., perhaps drawing pictures of such changes. The teacher might put the class's drawings together on a bulletin board entitled "How Our Community Is Changing." The teacher might encourage his class to continue to look for examples of change in their neighborhood, adding steadily to their bulletin board as the school year progresses and discussing at their level of maturity the ways in which such changes may affect their lives.

---

[9] Michihiko Hachiya, *Hiroshima Diary* (Chapel Hill, N.C.: The University of North Carolina Press, 1955), pp. 1, 8.
[10] Boston: Houghton Mifflin Co., 1942.

Similarly, primary grade children might be given simple "home-work" assignments in which they are asked to observe (on their way to or from school) all the changes *man* has made in their community or neighborhood. A related assignment might involve blocking out a given locality near the school as a class "observation area." The children could observe this area periodically throughout the year and note all the changes that take place, *why* they occur, and so forth. Other simple observation experiences for primary grade children might include an examination of a hillside washed away by a sudden rainstorm, a farm marred by erosion, a tree struck down by lightning or a severe windstorm, etc.

Children in both primary and intermediate grades might be intrigued with items from local and other newspapers in which nature's effects on the land are vividly portrayed both verbally and pictorially. An Oregon newspaper, for example, ran a frightening yet revealing picture story of recent disastrous flood damage in that area under this headline:

RAMPAGING RIVER CUTS NEW CHANNEL DOWN MT. HOOD [11]

A number of photographs clearly illustrate the destruction caused by the new course taken by the river—the homes, highways, campsites, and businesses destroyed, the many problems faced by the area's inhabitants, and so forth.

Another, gentler approach to an understanding of the many ways in which man and nature change the face of the earth might be built around the legendary character, Johnny Appleseed. The teacher could begin by reading any one of a number of good versions of the original story. After briefly discussing the legend, the teacher might tell his class that he is going to read them some things about Johnny Appleseed that were written by people who really knew him—people who had seen him come into their valley and watched him go about his work. The following passages from Louis Bromfield's "Johnny Appleseed and Aunt Mattie" could then be read:

The spirit of Johnny Appleseed haunted that same Valley. Once, long ago, he had roamed all the region, sleeping in the big sandstone caves or in Indian huts or settlers' cabins. He was welcome wherever he stopped among the Indians, the white settlers or the wild animals themselves.

. . .

He never accepted the hospitality of a bed but chose instead to sleep in the great haymows above the fat cattle and horses. Usually when the settler went to the barn in the morning Johnny had already vanished with his kettle on his head and his "poke" of apple and fennel

---

[11] The *Oregonian*, January 1, 1965.

seed thrown over his shoulder. I think every Indian, every settler, every trader in all that Ohio country must have known him well, much as my great-grandfather knew him.

. . .

In the next county there is an ancient apple tree which, it is claimed, was one of those planted by Johnny. I do not know whether this is true or not but I do know that in our pastures, on the edge of the woods and in the fence rows there are apple trees which are the descendants of those planted by Johnny. They bear a wide variety of apples from those which are small and bitter to those, on one or two trees, which are small but of a delicious wild flavor which no apples borne on respectable commercial apple trees ever attain. Their blossoms have a special perfume, very sweet and spicy, which you can smell a long way off, long before you come upon the trees themselves. They have been scattered here and there long ago by squirrels and rabbits and muskrat and raccoon who fed on the fruit of the trees planted more than a century and a half ago on the edge of clearings out of Johnny Appleseed's "poke."

And in our Valley, Johnny Appleseed is certainly not dead. He is there in the caves and the woodland, along the edge of the marshes and in hedgerows. When in early spring there drifts toward you the perfume of a wild apple tree, the spirit of Johnny rides the breeze. When in winter the snow beneath a wild apple tree is crisscrossed with the delicate prints of raccoon or muskrat or rabbit, you know that they have been there gathering apples from the trees that would never have existed but for crazy Johnny and his saucepan and "poke" of seeds. He is alive wherever the feathery fennel or the flowering day lilies cover a bank. He is there in the trees and the caves, the springs and the streams of our Ohio country, alive still in a legend which grows and grows.[12]

The teacher might discuss Bromfield's descriptions with his class, emphasizing, of course, the positive, unspectacular yet lasting nature of the changes Johnny brought about.

Literature may be used in a variety of ways to help students at all ages understand more fully the dynamic nature of the world's geography. While space does not permit an exhaustive treatment, perhaps the following passages will give the reader an idea of the flavor of the writing we have in mind.

The first passage appears in *When the Mountain Fell,* by C. F. Ramuz. The incident described took place in Switzerland.

Two months, or nearly two months, had passed. People had come to the mountain. They clambered over the great pile of rock. They had all the time they needed to hunt from one end to the other through the

---

[12] Abridgment of pp. 28–32, *Pleasant Valley,* by Louis Bromfield. Copyright 1945 by Louis Bromfield. Reprinted by permission of Harper & Row, Publishers.

tumbled stones of its surface. They found nothing. Nothing anywhere, not a single person, living or dead. Cabins, animals and men had disappeared completely under the stones.

Then came the Federal engineers, taking their turn after the doctor, the coroner, and the throngs of curious spectators. They were there to estimate the volume of the landslide: a hundred and fifty million cubic feet.

They, too, had all the time they needed while they took their measurements. They unrolled their long tapes, with the little black division marks, laying them flat against the rocks, first across the valley, then down its length. Then one of the men climbed to the top of what seemed to be the highest boulder in the mass, trying to estimate its depth.

They calculated the size of the avalanche so that the necessary changes could be made in the maps; so that what was indicated on the records as pastures and fertile fields could be replaced by the notation: "waste land."

The survey took a long time, but they had all the time in the world to complete it. No one interfered with them as they worked. The people who came out of curiosity grew fewer and fewer as the days went by, and the world of nature was peaceful and acquiescent, having returned to rest, to immobility, to indifference. Finally, last of all, came scientists from the city, who climbed up as far as the glacier and went carefully all over it, looking for any fresh crevasses that might spell a new danger, either imminent or in the distant future. But everything seemed to be securely in its proper place. . . .[13]

A second example comes from Alan Paton's classic, *Cry the Beloved Country*. The setting is, of course, South Africa.

Where you stand the grass is rich and matted, you cannot see the soil. But the rich green hills break down. They fall to the valley below, and falling, change their nature. For they grow red and bare; they cannot hold the rain and mist, and the streams are dry in the kloofs. Too many cattle feed upon the grass, and too many fires have burned it. Stand shod upon it, for it is coarse and sharp, and the stones cut under the feet. It is not kept, or guarded, or cared for, it no longer keeps men, guards men, cares for men. The titihoya does not cry here any more.

The great red hills stand desolate, and the earth has torn away like flesh. The lightning flashes over them, the clouds pour down upon them, the dead streams come to life, full of the red blood of the earth. Down in the valleys women scratch the soil that is left, and the maize hardly reaches the height of a man. They are valleys of old men and old women, of mothers and children. The men are away, the young men and the girls are away. The soil cannot keep them any more.[14]

---

[13] New York: Pantheon Books, Inc., 1947, pp. 99–100. Originally published in France by Editions Bernard Grasset under the title *Derborence*, © 1936.

[14] New York: Charles Scribner's Sons, 1950, pp. 3–4.

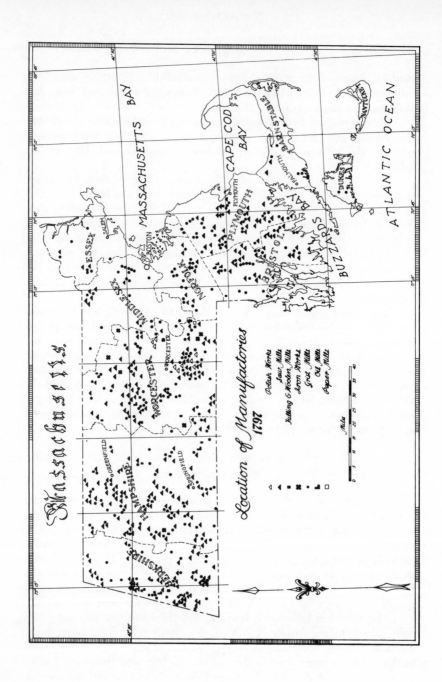

110

Perhaps one of the most fascinating studies ever undertaken in the field of geography was Ralph Brown's attempt to write a portrait of the Eastern Seaboard of the United States in 1810 as seen through the eyes of a geographer of the period. Brown did everything he could to immerse himself in the period about which he was writing, attempting to divorce himself completely from twentieth-century developments in his field. The book thus becomes a gold mine for teachers looking for material that might help their junior and senior high school students understand a variety of changes that have taken place in that area during the last century and a half.

For example, teachers might use simple descriptive material like the following as a basis for comparison:

> Connecticut is the most populous, in proportion to its extent, of any of the Thirteen States. It is laid out in small farms from fifty to three or four hundred acres each . . . The state is chequered with innumerable roads or high ways, crossing each other in every direction. A traveller, on any of these roads, even in the most unsettled parts of the state, will seldom pass more than two or three miles without finding a house or cottage . . . The whole state resembles a well cultivated garden.[15]

More complex opportunities for comparison lie in the accompanying map of the location of manufacturing industries in Massachusetts in 1810 (Fig. 15). Students might attempt to discover whether or not any of these industries still exist, what kinds of industries have been added, which have disappeared, and, above all, *why* these developments took place.

Still another approach to our generalization relating to change involves a series of studies in depth by senior high school students of carefully selected places whose character has been drastically altered by physical change. Using the school library, community libraries, and any other available sources, a group of students might investigate patterns of living in Panama before and after the construction of the canal. Other groups might investigate the changes that took place at Cape Kennedy following the installation of rocket facilities there, or the possible meaning to commuters, merchants, ferryboat owners and employees, and others of the construction of the new Verazzano Bridge in New York.

---

15 Ralph H. Brown, *Mirror for Americans* (New York: American Geographical Society, 1945), p. 29.

Fig. 15. From Ralph H. Brown, *Mirror for Americans* (New York: American Geographical Society, 1945), p. 74. Reproduced by courtesy of the *Geographical Review.*

An interesting side light to the above study might include a "brainstorming" session in which one of the world's "dead-end streets" is chosen as the stimulus for discussion. Suppose, for example, the class selected an area like Tierra Del Fuego, the barren, bleak, southernmost tip of South America. At present it enjoys neither site nor situational advantages. The class might attempt to suggest some possible *future* changes that could come about that would change the character of this relatively desolate place. The teacher could encourage his students to really go out on a limb, to be creative and imaginative, to try to avoid conventional thinking. The class might ultimately select four or five as most plausible.

Students at a variety of grade levels might both enjoy and profit from a study of the ghost towns of our American West. Small groups of students or, perhaps, individuals might choose from a list of ghost towns such as the following:

Washington
Copper City, Index, Sultan, Trinity, Liberty
Idaho
Silver City, Placerville, Pioneerville
Montana
Keystone, Elkhorn, Granite, Virginia City, Garnet
Colorado
Leadville, Silverton, Eureka, Gladstone
Nevada
Midas, Tuscarora, Austin, Belmont, Dayton, Fairview, Calico
California
Bodie, Masonic, Cerro Gordo, Darwin
Oregon
Hardman, Shaniko, Antelope, Cornucopia, Manesville, Bonanza

In each case the students would attempt to locate the town, discover why it grew and declined, as well as its current status. While there are a number of excellent books dealing with such places, Lambert Florin's *Western Ghost Towns* is an unusually readable and colorful source. The demise of Skamokawa, Washington, for example is described as follows:

Skamokawa reached its peak in the first years of this century. About 1910 there were about 400 to 500 people, a fine schoolhouse had been built and three large shingle mills operated full tilt. The first co-operative creamery in the state was operating. A newer section had sprung up closer to the river itself. New docks, an imposing store and a three-story hotel faced the water. To them came, several times daily, the steamboats of the day. Sidewheelers and sternwheelers they were; the Lurline, the Harvest Queen, the T. J. Potter and all the rest.

But when river traffic died, so did something in Skamokawa. The big hotel emptied and faded, the store windows now stare on a sagging dock, the planks of which are rotting away and returning to the river.[16]

A study of Skamokawa and other towns should reveal, among other things, that while a town often became a *ghost* town because of the depletion of mineral deposits, there were many *other* causes as well. Students could attempt to look at their own communities for the kinds of factors that might cause similar (if not so drastic) changes, perhaps concluding their study with a search for some twentieth-century ghost towns located in poverty stricken areas such as the Minnesota Iron Range or sections of Appalachia.

CONCLUSION

No student should walk away from his study of the earth without having gained some feeling for the mystery, majesty, and beauty of the diverse, ever changing environment that is in fact his home. Neither would a school's program in geography be successful if it failed to stimulate a lively curiosity about the earth's surface and the creatures that inhabit it. Students should come away from their studies with a recognition of the importance of location on the earth and with some comprehension of the complexity of the world in which they live, the problems and forces that both divide and unify it, as well as the principles that help us to understand it. Above all, however, children and youth should grapple with one of geography's age-old problems, i.e., *the nature of the relationship between man and his environment.*

Geographers themselves disagree as to the exact nature of this relationship. George F. Carter, for example, has expressed his views in these words: "The physical environment is but a stage on which the play is acted . . . it is at all times inert, impassive, non-compelling— unable to . . . urge, coax, encourage or discourage man. The environment simply exists." [17]

Other geographers would state the case differently. Professor Broek, the reader may recall, saw this crucial relationship as one in which "each society. . . perceives and interprets its physical surroundings through

---

[16] Lambert Florin, *Western Ghost Towns*, Seattle. Superior Publishing Company, 1961, pp. 21–22.

[17] George F. Carter, *Man and the Land* (New York: Holt, Rinehart & Winston, Inc., 1964), p. 5.

the prism of its own way of life. Only within this perceptual framework can the physical environment influence man."

All would agree, however, that geography considers the earth as the world of man. Even in the study of the earth's physical features— its mountains and valleys, its deserts and oceans, its plateaus and plains— the student must never lose sight of man, who uses and molds them to suit his purpose. In the final analysis it is the *human mind,* not the physical environment, that determines the ways in which life is lived on this planet. An understanding of this idea points the way toward a richer, fuller life for all the earth's inhabitants.

INDEX